PE
chemical
engineering

practice exam

978-1-932613-52-0

ISBN 978-1-932613-52-0

Printed in the United States of America
4th printing November 2014

CONTENTS

About NCEES

The National Council of Examiners for Engineering and Surveying (NCEES) is a nonprofit organization made up of engineering and surveying licensing boards from all U.S. states and territories. Since its founding in 1920, NCEES has been committed to advancing licensure for engineers and surveyors in order to protect the health, safety, and welfare of the American public.

NCEES helps its member licensing boards carry out their duties to regulate the professions of engineering and surveying. It develops best-practice models for state licensure laws and regulations and promotes uniformity among the states. It develops and administers the exams used for engineering and surveying licensure throughout the country. It also provides services to help licensed engineers and surveyors practice their professions in other U.S. states and territories.

Updates on exam content and procedures

Visit us at **ncees.org/exams** for updates on everything exam-related, including specifications, exam-day policies, scoring, and corrections to published exam preparation materials. This is also where you will register for the exam and find additional steps you should follow in your state to be approved for the exam.

Exam-day schedule

Be sure to arrive at the exam site on time. Late-arriving examinees will not be allowed into the exam room once the proctor has begun to read the exam script. The report time for the exam will be printed on your Exam Authorization. Normally, you will be given 1 hour between morning and afternoon sessions.

Admission to the exam site

To be admitted to the exam, you must bring two items: (1) your Exam Authorization and (2) a current, signed, government-issued identification.

Examinee Guide

The *NCEES Examinee Guide* is the official guide to policies and procedures for all NCEES exams. All examinees are required to read this document before starting the exam registration process. You can download it at ncees.org/exams. It is your responsibility to make sure that you have the current version.

NCEES exams are administered in either a computer-based format or a pencil-and-paper format. Each method of administration has specific rules. This guide describes the rules for each exam format. Refer to the appropriate section for your exam.

Scoring and reporting

NCEES typically releases exam results to its member licensing boards 8–10 weeks after the exam. Depending on your state, you will be notified of your exam result online through your MyNCEES account or via postal mail from your state licensing board. Detailed information on the scoring process can be found at ncees.org/exams.

Staying connected

To keep up to date with NCEES announcements, events, and activities, connect with us on your preferred social media network.

EXAM SPECIFICATIONS

NCEES Principles and Practice of Engineering Examination
CHEMICAL Exam Specifications
EFFECTIVE Beginning with the April 2011 Examinations

- The exam is an 8-hour open-book exam. It contains 40 multiple-choice questions in the 4-hour morning session, and 40 multiple-choice questions in the 4-hour afternoon session. Examinee works all questions.

- The exam uses both the International System of units (SI) and the US Customary System (USCS).

- The exam is developed with questions that will require a variety of approaches and methodologies including design, analysis, and application. Some questions may require knowledge of engineering economics.

- The knowledge areas specified as examples of kinds of knowledge are not exclusive or exhaustive categories.

	Approximate Number of Questions

I. Mass/Energy Balances and Thermodynamics — **18**

A. Mass Balances — 8
  1. Material balances with no reaction (e.g., phase behavior; mass; volume; density; composition; purge; bypass)
  2. Material balances with reaction (e.g., multiple reactions; incomplete reactions; excess reactant; purge; bypass; recycle; combustion)

B. Energy Balances and Thermodynamics — 10
  1 Energy balances on non-reactive systems (e.g., sensible heat; latent heat; heat of solution)
  2 Energy balances on reactive systems (e.g., heat of reaction and combinations with sensible heat; latent heat; heat of solution)
  3. Power cycles (e.g., refrigeration; engines; turbines; heat recovery)

II. Heat Transfer — **13**

A. Mechanisms — 7
  1. Heat transfer without phase change (e.g., thermal conductivity; heat capacity; conduction; convection: free/forced heat transfer coefficients/correlations; radiation; combinations thereof)
  2. Heat transfer with phase change (e.g., vaporization and evaporation; condensation; sublimation; crystallization; latent heat)

B. Applications — 6
  1. Heat exchange equipment design (e.g., overall heat transfer coefficient; fouling factors; LMTD; F-factor; equipment selection; insulation)
  2. Heat exchange equipment analysis (e.g., pressure drop; fouling effects; performance evaluation (NTU); changes in parameters)

III. Kinetics — **9**

A. Reaction Parameters — 5
  1. Rate equation (e.g., rate constant, activation energy; order of reaction; mechanisms; catalysis)
  2. Chemical equilibria (e.g., temperature and pressure dependence; composition)

B. Reactors — 4
  1. Conversion in single reactors [e.g., batch reactor; continuous stirred tank reactor (CSTR); plug flow reactor (PFR)]

2. Conversion in complex reactors (e.g. reactors in series: CSTR and/or PFR; multiphase reactors; fluidized beds; packed beds; recycle, bioreactors)
3. Yield and selectivity

IV. Fluids   13
A. Mechanical-Energy Balance   10
1. Flow behavior (e.g., viscosity; velocity; Reynolds number; friction factor; pressure drop in pipes, valves, and fittings; expansion/contraction; porous media; particle dynamics; fluidization; sonic velocity; laminar/turbulent; two-phase flow)
2. Flow applications (e.g., potential and kinetic energy; friction; flow networks; mixing; pumps; NPSH, turbines; compressors; drivers; solids handling)
B. Flow and Pressure Measurement Techniques   3
1. Flow measurement application (e.g., mass and volumetric meters) and pressure measurement application (e.g., permanent pressure drop; differential pressure devices)

V. Mass Transfer   11
A. Phase Equilibria   4
1. Ideal systems (e.g., Henry's Law; Raoult's Law; Dalton's Law; ideal gas law; vapor pressure)
2. Non-ideal systems (e.g., activity coefficients; fugacity coefficients; azeotropes; immiscible/partially miscible phases; equations of state)
3. Phase equilibrium applications (e.g., bubble point; dew point; flash; critical states)
B. Continuous Vapor-Liquid Contactors   6
1. Material and energy balances for trayed units and packed units (e.g., absorption; stripping; distillation)
2. Design parameters for trayed units (e.g., minimum flow rates and reflux; minimum and theoretical stages; feed location; tray selection; capacity/efficiency; flooding; dumping; tray hydraulics)
3. Design parameters for non-trayed units (e.g., minimum flow rates and reflux; minimum stages; theoretical stages/NTU; feed location; packing selection; capacity/efficiency; flooding; pressure drop; mass transfer coefficients/height of transfer units)
C. Miscellaneous Mass Transfer Processes   1
1. Continuous, batch and semi-continuous (e.g., drying; membranes; extraction; crystallization; filtration; leaching; humidification; diffusion, adsorption; absorption; stripping; distillation)

VI. Plant Design and Operation   16
A. Economic Considerations   1
1. Cost estimation and project evaluation (e.g., capital costs; depreciation; operating costs; risk evaluation; optimization; return on investment)
B. Design   8
1. Process design (e.g., process flow sheets; P&ID; specifications; procedures; modeling/simulation; scale-up; process or product development; boundary conditions)

2. Process equipment design (e.g., equipment selection; optimization; design temperature; design pressure)

3. Siting considerations (e.g., security; ingress; egress; plant layout; utilities; natural disasters; human factors)

4. Instrumentation and process control (e.g., sensors; controller actions; feed-back/feed-forward actions)

5. Materials of construction (e.g., material properties and selection; corrosion considerations)

C. Operation   3

1. Process and equipment reliability (e.g., testing; preventative maintenance; start-up/shut-down procedures; robustness)

2. Process improvement and troubleshooting (e.g., debottlenecking; experimental design and evaluation; optimization)

D. Safety, Health, and Environment   4

1. Protection systems [e.g., pressure/vacuum relief valves (safety valves); flares; rupture disks; vents; vacuum breakers; inerting; seal legs; discharge location; configuration; fire protection]

2. Industrial hygiene (e.g., MSDS; exposure limits and control; noise control; ventilation; personal protective equipment)

3. Hazard identification and management [e.g., flammability/explosive limits; auto-ignition; reactor stability; process hazard analysis; safety integrity level (SIL); management of change]

4. Environmental considerations (e.g., emissions evaluation; permitting; pollution prevention; mitigation; waste determination)

101. Orimulsion is a tar-like bitumen that uses an emulsifying agent to produce a liquid. This blend (15 wt% emulsifying agent) can be substituted for oil in utility burners.

Data on orimulsion (exclusive of emulsifying agent):

Heating Value: 16,800 Btu/lb (dry and ash-free)
Content, wt%:
    Ash: 12.1
    Moisture: 10.9
    Organic: 77.0

The emulsifying agent has no heating value. The heating value (Btu/lb) of the as-delivered emulsified fuel is most nearly:

(A)   11,000
(B)   12,900
(C)   14,300
(D)   16,800

102. The line separating the solid phase from the liquid phase on the pressure–temperature (P–T) phase diagram below has a negative slope. What is the reason for this behavior?

(A)   The density of the solid is less than that of the liquid.

(B)   The heat of fusion is negative.

(C)   The specific volume of the solid is less than that of the liquid.

(D)   The solid forms only at temperatures below 0°C.

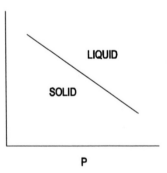

103. The table below gives the characteristics of a gas stream flowing at a rate of 100 lb moles/hr.

Component	MW	mol%
N_2	28	80
SO_2	64	20

The N_2 flow rate (lb/hr) is most nearly:

(A)   80
(B)   2,250
(C)   2,800
(D)   3,500

104. Pure KNO_3 is made from a crude salt mixture (99 wt% KNO_3 and 1 wt% NaCl) by the process illustrated below. The solubility of KNO_3 at 30°C is 45.8 lb per 100 lb water and at 70°C is 138 lb/100 lb water. The flow rate (lb/min) of the recycle is most nearly:

(A)   50
(B)   85
(C)   100
(D)   135

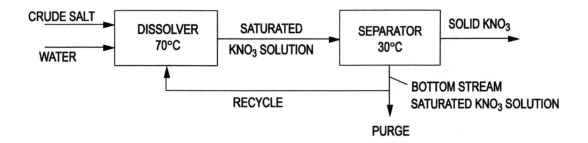

Material Balance (lb/min)				
Parameter	Crude Salt	Water	KNO₃ Product	Purge
KNO_3	99	—	83.6	15.4
NaCl	1	—	—	1
Water	—	33.6	—	33.6
Total	100	33.6	83.6	50.0

105. A binary mixture of tetrahydrofuran (THF) and isopropyl alcohol (IPA) is to be separated into relatively pure streams of THF and IPA in a distillation column operating at atmospheric pressure. The column material balance is summarized in the table below.

Components	Material Balance (lb mole/hr)		
	Streams		
	Feed F	Distillate D	Bottoms B
THF	0.5459	0.4914	0.0545
IPA	1.2165	0.0120	1.2045
Total	1.7624	0.5034	1.2590
THF, mole %	30.97	97.61	4.33
IPA, mole %	69.03	2.39	95.67

For a stripping-section molar L/V ratio of 1.40, the vapor leaving the kettle reboiler has a flow rate (lb mole/hr) of most nearly:

(A) 3.15
(B) 1.76
(C) 0.90
(D) 0.52

106. A fuel contains 80 wt% carbon (C) and 20 wt% hydrogen (H). Combustion results in the following composition by volume (dry basis):

CO_2	9.41
CO	1.69
O_2	3.8
N_2	85.1

The following equations describe the chemical reactions taking place:

$$CO + 0.5\,O_2 \rightarrow CO_2$$
$$C + O_2 \rightarrow CO_2$$
$$H_2 + 0.5\,O_2 \rightarrow H_2O$$
$$C + 0.5\,O_2 \rightarrow CO$$

On the basis of 100 lb moles of dry flue gas, the O_2 required (lb moles) for complete combustion is most nearly:

(A) 11.1
(B) 18.6
(C) 19.4
(D) 27.8

107. Chlorobenzene (monochlorobenzene, MCB) and chlorine (Cl) are reacted to produce dichlorobenzenes (DCBs), with some undesirable trichlorobenzenes (TCBs) being produced. In addition to the reactor, a separation system is provided to recover the unreacted MCB and the desired DCB products and remove the trichlorinated material and the HCl by-product.

$$MCB + Cl_2\,(g) \rightarrow DCB + HCl\,(g)$$
$$DCB + Cl_2\,(g) \rightarrow TCB + HCl\,(g)$$

The plant operates with a ratio of recycle MCB to fresh feed MCB of 0.90. The ratio of DCBs to TCBs is 15:1. The one-pass conversion of MCB for the plant is most nearly:

(A) 6.2%
(B) 47%
(C) 53%
(D) 94%

108. Methyl mercaptan (CH_3SH) is produced from **stoichiometric** amounts of H_2S and methanol (CH_3OH) by the reaction:

$$CH_3OH + H_2S \rightarrow CH_3SH + H_2O$$

The H_2S selectivity (percentage of the total conversion to the desired product) is 90%. The other products are formed from the reaction of methanol and H_2S. Of the feed to the reactor (fresh feed plus recycle), 85% reacts on each pass through the reactor. The unreacted feed containing stoichiometric amounts of H_2S and methanol is recycled.

Molecular Weights:

CH_3OH	32.0
H_2S	34.1
CH_3SH	48.1
H_2O	18.0

The fresh feed (lb mole/hr) of H_2S required to produce 1,000 lb/hr of mercaptan is most nearly:

(A)   19
(B)   21
(C)   23
(D)   27

109. The refrigerant HFC-134a is contained in a rigid vessel at $p = 20$ MPa and 150°C. It is cooled in a batch process until the pressure is 3.5 MPa. Which of the following best represents the final conditions?

(A)   Vapor-liquid mixture

(B)   Superheated vapor

(C)   Saturated liquid

(D)   Subcooled liquid

       GO ON TO THE NEXT PAGE

109. (Continued)

30.16

2009 ASHRAE Handbook—Fundamentals (SI)

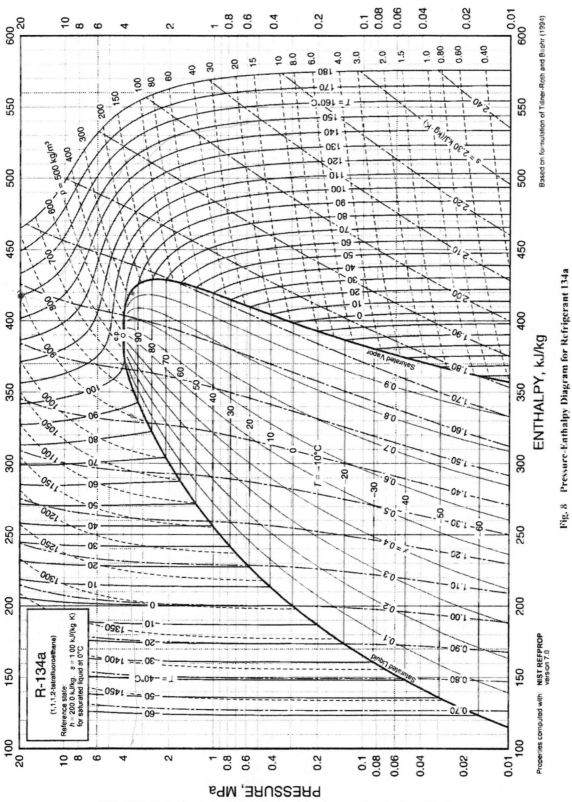

Fig. 8 Pressure-Enthalpy Diagram for Refrigerant 134a

2009 ASHRAE Handbook–Fundamentals (SI), p. 30.16, © American Society of Heating,
Refrigerating, and Air-Conditioning Engineers, Inc., www.ashrae.org.

110. A light oil enters a heat exchanger at 240°F and at a flow rate of 8,600 lb/hr. Cooling water at 45°F enters this countercurrent heat exchanger and leaves at 110°F.

> Heat capacity of oil = 0.55 Btu/(lb-F)
> Heat capacity of water = 1.00 Btu/(lb-F)

If the heat duty is 480,000 Btu/hr, the cooling water flow rate (lb/hr) is most nearly:

(A) 4,730
(B) 7,380
(C) 13,400
(D) 15,600

111. The figure shows an enthalpy-concentration chart for water. The heat evolved (Btu) when 50 lb of water is mixed with 100 lb of sulfuric acid at 77°F and with a final solution temperature of 77°F is most nearly:

(A)   2,750
(B)   16,000
(C)   18,750
(D)   21,500

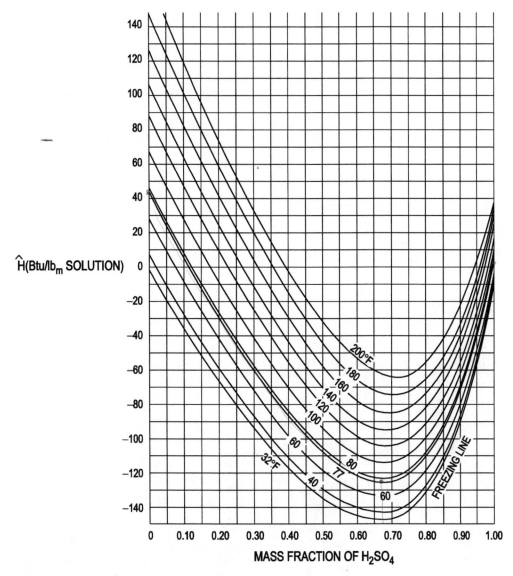

MASS FRACTION OF H$_2$SO$_4$

ENTHALPY-CONCENTRATION CHART FOR H$_2$SO$_4$–H$_2$O

Used by permission. Original work by W.D. Ross, *Chemical Engineering Progress*, American Institute of Chemical Engineers, 43:314, 1952.
Reproduced in Smith and Van Ness, *Introduction to Chemical Engineering Thermodynamics*, 4th ed., McGraw-Hill, 1987, p. 441.

112. Air enters a countercurrent dryer at a flow rate of 1,000 kg/s (dry basis) at 405 K. The humidity of the entering air is 7.0 g moisture/kg dry air. The reference temperature is 298 K. The following data are available:

Heat capacity of dry air	0.99 kJ/(kg·K)
Heat capacity of water vapor	2.01 kJ/(kg·K)
Heat capacity of liquid water	4.186 kJ/(kg·K)
Latent heat of vaporization of water at 298 K	2,442 kJ/kg

The enthalpy of the incoming air (MJ/s) is most nearly:

(A)   107
(B)   124
(C)   401
(D)   424

113. The vapor pressure of 2,2,4-trimethyl pentane at several temperatures is given below.

Temperature (°F)	Vapor pressure (atm)
45.5	0.0263
69.3	0.0526
84.4	0.0789
105.3	0.1316

The heat of vaporization (Btu/lb mole) of this compound at 77°F is most nearly:

(A)   310
(B)   1,000
(C)   6,700
(D)   15,000

114. Propylene glycol is produced by the hydrolysis of propylene oxide (PO) in the liquid phase:

$$CH_3CHOCH_2 + H_2O \rightarrow CH_3CHOHCH_2OH$$

This exothermic reaction occurs readily at room temperature when catalyzed by sulfuric acid. The feed is a stream of 24,000 kg/hr with the following composition:

Propylene oxide	10 wt%
Sulfuric acid	1 wt%
Water	89 wt%

Other data are:

Heat capacity of the reaction mixture	4.18 kJ/(kg•K)
Heat of reaction	−1,459 kJ/kg PO

If an adiabatic reactor is used to achieve a fractional conversion of 0.8 for PO with a feed temperature of 20°C, the reactor exit temperature is most nearly:

(A) 265 K
(B) 295 K
(C) 300 K
(D) 320 K

115. The standard heats of formation of ammonia (NH_3), nitric oxide (NO), and water (H_2O), all in the gaseous state, are −11.05, 21.60, and −57.80 kcal/g mole, respectively. The standard heat of reaction for the complete oxidation of ammonia with oxygen to nitric oxide and water vapor (kJ/mol) is most nearly:

(A) −905
(B) −226
(C) −54
(D) 46

116. To compute the distribution of a volatile solute between a hydrocarbon polymer phase (e.g., polybutene) and the vapor phase, a weight fraction activity coefficient (Ω) is used. The activity of the solute in the liquid phase is:

$$a_{solute} = w_{solute}\Omega$$

where:

w_{solute} is the weight fraction of the solute in the polymer.

The weight fraction activity coefficient has the advantage of being nearly constant over a wide range of temperatures and nearly linear in weight fractions below 0.1. What is the reason for using a weight fraction activity coefficient for solutes in a polymer?

(A)   The vapor pressure of polymers is very low.

(B)   The viscosity of concentrated polymer solutions is high.

(C)   The density of the polymer is different from the density of the solute.

(D)   The molecular weight of a polymer is an undefinable value, unlike the solute.

117. The power plant shown in the figure uses an ideal reheat cycle (Rankine cycle with reheat as shown in the figure). According to the h-s diagram provided on the following page, the quality of the steam after the second expansion to 3.0 in. Hg absolute is most nearly:

(A)   1.00
(B)   0.90
(C)   0.09
(D)   0.009

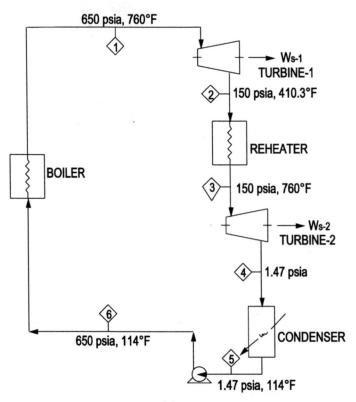

117. (Continued)

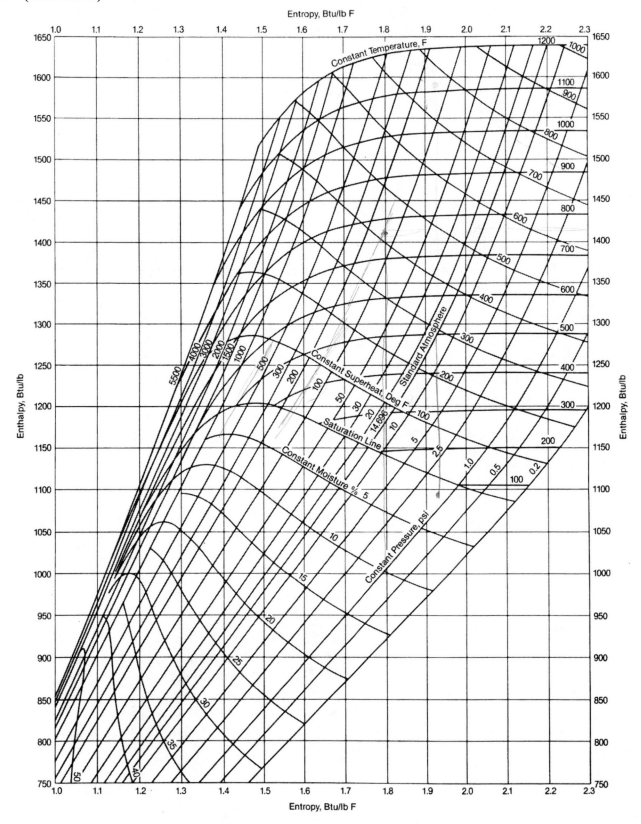

Courtesy of The Babcock & Wilcox Company.

118. In a chemical process, superheated steam at 250 psia and 800°F expands through a reversible, well-insulated turbo-expander to 2.89 psia. The shaft work produced is the enthalpy difference between the inlet and outlet streams. The shaft work produced by the turbo-expander (Btu/lb) in this process is most nearly:

(A)   10
(B)   300
(C)   400
(D)   1,200

119. A thermopane window is one in which two pieces of glass are separated by a stagnant air layer. The following data apply:

Inside and outside convection coefficients	1 Btu/(hr-ft^2-F)
Thermal conductivity of glass	0.5 Btu/(hr-ft-F)
Thermal conductivity of air	0.015 Btu/(hr-ft-F)
Glass thickness	0.25 in.
Air gap for thermopane	0.25 in.

The ratio of the heat flux for a thermopane to that for a single glass pane is most nearly:

(A)   0.13
(B)   0.59
(C)   0.98
(D)   1.7

120. A vertical-cylindrical furnace has an outside diameter of 33'-4" and is 12 ft high. The outside wall temperature is 1,200°F. The furnace has 30 in. of insulation applied [$k = 1$ Btu/(hr-ft-F)]. The exterior surface of the insulation is 77°F. The energy loss (Btu/hr) through the cylindrical wall of the furnace is most nearly:

(A)   51,000
(B)   560,000
(C)   610,000
(D) 1,500,000

121. An air stream is flowing over a thin, smooth flat plate that has a dimension of 1.0 ft in the direction of the flow. The heat-transfer coefficient between the flat plate and the air stream is obtained from the following expression:

$$N_{Nu} = 0.664 \, (N_{Re})^{0.5} \, (N_{Pr})^{0.33}$$

where: N_{Nu} = Nusselt number
N_{Re} = Reynolds number
N_{Pr} = Prandtl number

The thermal conductivity of air is 0.0156 Btu/(hr-ft-F).

If the Reynolds number for the flow of air over the flat plate is 3×10^5 and the Prandtl number is 0.9, then the heat-transfer coefficient [Btu/(hr-ft^2-F)] is most nearly:

(A) 0.6
(B) 5.5
(C) 8.3
(D) 350

122. A liquid is stored in a large-diameter tank that is maintained at 190°F. The tank is constructed of 1.5-in.-thick carbon steel plate [k = 23 Btu/(hr-ft-F)]. The convective heat-transfer coefficients are:

Inside of tank h = 30 Btu/(hr-ft^2-F)
Exterior of tank h = 10 Btu/(hr-ft^2-F)

The cold design air temperature is –20°F. For a fouled interior tank wall (R = 0.01 hr-ft^2-F/Btu), the heat loss flux [Btu/(hr-ft^2)] is most nearly:

(A) 1,140
(B) 1,420
(C) 1,470
(D) 1,510

123. The black flat roof of a building has an absorptivity of 0.8 for solar radiation. At midday the sun has an intensity of 300 Btu/(ft²-hr). Assume that the temperature of the air and of the surroundings is 80°F, the wind velocity is negligible, and no heat penetrates the roof from inside the building. The rate of heat transfer by conduction-convection Q/A [Btu/(ft²-hr)] can be assumed to be $0.38(\Delta T)^{1.25}$, where ΔT is the temperature difference (°F) between the roof and the air. Under these conditions, the equilibrium (or steady-state) temperature on the roof is 177.5°F. The percentage of the heat that is lost from the roof by radiation is most nearly:

(A) 52%
(B) 61%
(C) 80%
(D) 85%

124. Boiling heat-transfer coefficients are a function of the temperature difference (ΔT) between the boiling fluid and the heated surface. Considering a ΔT ranging between 10° and 1,000°, the qualitative behavior of the heat flux (Q/A) versus ΔT is given by which of the curves below?

(A)

(B)

(C)

(D)

GO ON TO THE NEXT PAGE

125. A process stream is condensed, and the heat released is used to produce steam in a countercurrent heat exchanger. The process stream condenses at 465°F. Feedwater enters the heat exchanger at 120°F with saturated steam being produced at 440°F.

$$h_L = \quad 89 \text{ Btu/lb at } 120°F$$
$$h_L = \quad 419 \text{ Btu/lb at } 440°F$$
$$H_V = 1{,}205 \text{ Btu/lb at } 440°F$$

The percentage of the heat transferred to the water that is used to heat the liquid (sensible heat) is most nearly:

(A)   0%
(B)   30%
(C)   42%
(D)   70%

126. A binary liquid mixture of acetaldehyde and ethyl ether is to be processed in a batch distillation column. The still operates at 90 psig, and at this pressure the boiling points of acetaldehyde and ethyl ether are 131°F and 158°F, respectively. At 30 psig, the minimum-boiling azeotrope forms at 126.7°F.

The unit is equipped with a 50-ft^2 condenser [U_o = 155 Btu/(hr-ft^2-F)]. Cooling water is available at a design temperature of 85°F with a **maximum** discharge temperature of 124°F. The condenser duty is 282,500 Btu/hr. The outlet water temperature from the condenser is most nearly:

(A)   90°F
(B)   95°F
(C)   103°F
(D)   117°F

127. A tank is maintained at 250°F using 50-psig saturated steam. The tank heat loss is 75,000 Btu/hr and is compensated for by using a 1-in. Sch. 40 pipe worm heater. The following data apply:

Convective Heat-Transfer Coefficients:
  Condensing steam, h 1,200 Btu/(hr-ft^2-F)
  Exterior of pipe-to-fluid, h 40 Btu/(hr-ft^2-F)

Pipe Data:
  Thermal conductivity   26 Btu/(hr-ft-F)
  Interior pipe diameter   1.049 in.
  Exterior pipe diameter   1.315 in.

The length (ft) of pipe needed for the worm heater is most nearly:

(A)   10
(B)   120
(C)   190
(D)   380

128. An evaporator with a heat transfer area of 900 ft^2 and a heat transfer coefficient of 400 Btu/(hr-ft^2-F) is used to produce distilled water. The water, preheated to saturation, is fed to the evaporator, which operates at 1 atm. Saturated steam is used to convert the water to steam. The pressure in the steam jacket is maintained at 20 psig. The steam flow rate (lb/hr) to the evaporator is most nearly:

(A)   6,000
(B)   14,600
(C)   17,600
(D)   18,100

129. Compressed ammonia vapor (252 psia and 255°F) is to be totally condensed (247 psia and 110°F). The liquid ammonia is maintained at a constant temperature of 110°F. The ammonia flow rate is 17,250 lb/hr. Cooling tower water at 80°F is to be used in a countercurrent flow arrangement. The maximum design return water temperature is 125°F. The heat-release curve shown below applies. The following enthalpy data applies to the ammonia:

H_V (252 psia, 255°F)	733.3 Btu/lb
H_V (247 psia, 110°F)	633.7 Btu/lb
h_1 (247 psia, 110°F)	167.0 Btu/lb

The **maximum** cooling water discharge temperature from the condenser at **minimum** water flow is most nearly:

(A) 110°F
(B) 116°F
(C) 125°F
(D) 255°F

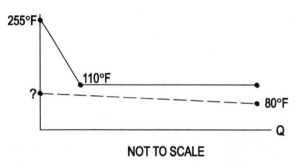

NOT TO SCALE

130. An exothermic reactor has a vertical orientation with a diameter of 10 1/2 ft (shell outside diameter) and a straight side height of 30 ft. The process precludes the use of external insulation, so a layer of recrystallized silicon carbide brick is used on the inside. The refractory develops a thin coating due to a carbon lay-down (fouling).

Data:

Thermal conductivity of silicon carbide brick	8.0 Btu/(hr-ft-F)
Thickness of the silicon carbide brick	6 in.
Thermal conductivity of steel	26 Btu/(hr-ft-F)
Thickness of the steel shell	1.5 in.
Natural convection/radiation heat transfer coefficient	1.5 Btu/(hr-ft²-F)
Ambient temperature	75°F
Temperature of exposed carbon layer surface	2,150°F
Heat flux	650 Btu/(hr-ft²)

Assuming that the reactor can be represented as a flat surface, the fouling heat-transfer coefficient h_{foul} [Btu/(hr-ft²-F)] for the carbon layer is most nearly:

(A) 0.40
(B) 1.36
(C) 1.50
(D) 2.46

131. A cooling water exchanger is used to cool a constant volumetric flow of gas. Only sensible cooling occurs. The following information is given:

Component	Inlet (°F)	Outlet (°F)
Cooling water	80	100
Gas	160	140

If the molecular weight of the gas is increased by 20%, what will happen?

(A)   The gas outlet temperature will increase, but the water outlet temperature will decrease.

(B)   The gas outlet temperature will decrease, but the water outlet temperature will increase.

(C)   The gas and water outlet temperatures will both increase.

(D)   The gas and water outlet temperature will both decrease.

132. A heterogenous catalytic chemical reaction between gaseous reactants A and B in the presence of a solid catalyst and with the overall stoichiometry of $A + B \rightarrow$ Products has the following overall equation: $-dP_A/dt = kP_AP_B/(1 + KP_A)$. Here, k and K are constants, and P_A and P_B represent the partial pressures of reactants A and B, respectively, in the gaseous phase. One can conclude from this rate expression that this chemical reaction occurs between:

(A)   gaseous reactant B and adsorbed reactant A on the catalyst surface

(B)   gaseous reactant A and adsorbed reactant B on the catalyst surface

(C)   reactants A and B, both adsorbed on the catalyst surface

(D)   reactants A and B exclusively in the gaseous phase

133. Reactants A and B undergo the following reaction:

$$A + B \rightarrow AB$$

The proposed mechanism for the overall reaction involves the following two reversible reactions:

$$A \leftrightarrow A*$$
$$A* + B \leftrightarrow AB$$

However, the reverse reaction rate for the second reaction is thought to be negligible compared to all other reactions. In terms of concentrations C_A, C_B, C_{AB} with a_1, a_2, and a_3 being constants to be empirically determined, the rate of formation of AB, r_{AB}, will be most likely:

(A) $r_{AB} = a_1 \, C_A \, C_B$

(B) $r_{AB} = a_1 C_A + a_2 \, C_{AB}$

(C) $r_{AB} = a_1 C_A \, C_B / (1 + a_2 C_B)$

(D) $r_{AB} = (a_1 C_A C_B - a_2 C_{AB})/(1 + a_3 C_B)$

134. An elementary, irreversible gas-phase reaction has the following form:

$$2A \rightarrow \text{products}$$

The rate expression for the reaction is written in terms of the partial pressure of the reactant (P_A):

$$-\frac{dP_A}{dt} = kP_A^2$$

where the rate constant k is 0.2 atm^{-1}-hr^{-1} at a temperature of 100°F and atmospheric pressure. The value of this rate constant [ft^3/(lb mole-hr)] is most nearly:

(A) 14.6
(B) 81.8
(C) 1,202
(D) 33,400

135. Phosphorus pentoxide is dissolved in water to form phosphoric acid. The following equilibrium reaction occurs in the aqueous solution:

$$H_3PO_4 \leftrightarrow H^+ + H_2PO_4^- \qquad\qquad K_1 = 7.516 \times 10^{-3}$$

The acid dissociation constant based on mol/L units is $\gamma_\pm = 0.8$. The concentration of $H_2PO_4^-$ (mol/L) present in a 1.0 F solution of phosphoric acid is most nearly:

(A)   0.897
(B)   0.103
(C)   0.083
(D)   0.0075

136. A waste-processing reactor filled with molten iron at 1,873 K is used for dissociating plastic-covered aluminum wire into its constituent elements. Oxygen is bubbled through the bath to oxidize the organic constituents into synthesis gas containing CO, CO_2, H_2, and H_2O. The metals leave the reactor either as iron alloy or as oxides partitioned between the ceramic phase and the iron-alloy phase.

Gibbs free energies (standard free energy of formation) for the oxidation of the elements to their oxides are presented in the table below. The values are for the reaction of 1.0 mole of oxygen with the stoichiometric amount of the element for the oxide listed. Melting points of metals and oxides are also indicated. Most of the aluminum is expected to exit the reactor as:

(A)   Al(l)

(B)   Al(s)

(C) Al_2O_3(s)

(D)   (Al·Fe) *alloy*

Compound	Free Energy, kJ/mol O_2 (1,873 K)	Melting Point (K)
FeO	−300	1,653
CO_2	−400	—
CO	−550	—
Al	—	933
Al_2O_3	−700	2,318
Fe	—	1,803

GO ON TO THE NEXT PAGE

137. You are to design an isothermal reactor system for a constant-density, liquid-phase, solid-catalyzed reaction $A \rightarrow B + C$. This reaction has the following rate equation:

$$r_B = \frac{k_1 C_A}{1 + k_2 C_A}$$

Data: $k_1 = 15 \text{ hr}^{-1}$

$k_2 = 16 \text{ ft}^3/(\text{lb mole})$

Concentration of A in feed stream, $C_{A_0} = 0.25$ lb mole/ft^3

Fractional conversion, $X_A = 0.9$

The space time (hr) in a plug-flow reactor for this service would be most nearly:

(A) 0.84
(B) 0.39
(C) 0.15
(D) 0.086

138. The liquid-phase reaction $A + B \rightarrow P$ is second order and irreversible. Catalyst C is needed in the reaction so that:

$C + B \rightarrow C \cdot B$ (fast)
$A + C \cdot B \rightarrow P \cdot C$ (slow)
$P \cdot C \rightarrow C + P$ (fast)

The reaction rate expression is found to be $-r_A = k\, C_A\, C_{C \cdot B}$.

Data: $k = 1.2 \times 10^{-6} \text{ m}^3/(\text{kmol·s})$

$C_{A_0} = 50 \text{ kmol/m}^3$

$C_{C_0} = 7 \text{ kmol/m}^3$

Assume there is sufficient reactant B to form the $C \cdot B$ complex. At 30% conversion of A in an ideal CSTR, the reaction rate [kmol/(m^3·s)] is most nearly:

(A) 1.26×10^{-4}
(B) 2.06×10^{-4}
(C) 2.94×10^{-4}
(D) 4.20×10^{-4}

     GO ON TO THE NEXT PAGE

139. The liquid-phase reaction C → D is being considered for a chemical process. The reaction occurs with 80% conversion of the reactant. The reaction rate constant value is 0.0095 sec^{-1} at the reaction temperature. For two identical CSTRs in series, the space time (min) for **each** CSTR is most nearly:

(A) 2.2
(B) 4.4
(C) 105
(D) 130

140. A catalytic process for the removal of SO_2 from flue gas by reducing the SO_2 to elemental sulfur using methane has been tested. The desired reaction is:

$$2\ SO_2 + CH_4 \rightarrow CO_2 + 2\ H_2O + 2\ S \quad \text{(Reaction 1)}$$

An undesired side reaction is:

$$SO_2 + 2\ CH_4 \rightarrow H_2S + 2\ CO + 3\ H_2 \quad \text{(Reaction 2)}$$

Rate expression and activation energy information are tabulated below:

Reaction	Rate Expression	Activation Energy (cal/mol)
1	$(-r_{SO_2})_1 = k_1 C^2_{SO_2}$	15,000
2	$(-r_{SO_2})_2 = k_2 C_{SO_2}$	5,000

In order to enhance the rate of the desired forward reaction relative to that of the undesired side reaction, which of the following strategies should be adopted?

(A) Increase both the reaction temperature and the concentration of SO_2 in the feed.

(B) Increase the reaction temperature and decrease the concentration of SO_2 in the feed.

(C) Decrease the reaction temperature and increase the concentration of SO_2 in the feed.

(D) Decrease both the reaction temperature and the concentration of SO_2 in the feed.

This completes the morning session. Solutions begin on page 53.

501. A pipeline from a refinery in El Paso, Texas, to a tank farm in Tucson, Arizona, carries four different brands and three different grades of gasoline on an alternating schedule. To minimize cross-contamination of grades and/or brands during transit through the pipeline, the flow in the pipeline should be:

    (A)   laminar

    (B)   transitional

    (C)   minimally turbulent

    (D)   highly turbulent

502. The pressure drop in a 6-in. pipe (I.D. = 6.065 in.) of length L is 1 psi with the flow in the highly turbulent region. If the same liquid flows at the same volumetric flow rate in a 3-in. pipe (I.D. = 3.068 in.) with length L, the pressure drop (psi) is most nearly:

    (A)   0.033
    (B)   2.0
    (C)   7.7
    (D)   30

503. Which of the following statements is correct for laminar flow of a liquid in a tube of unknown roughness?

    (A)   The transition from laminar to turbulent flow occurs at a Reynolds number of 210.

    (B)   The friction factor decreases when the Reynolds number increases.

    (C)   The friction factor depends on the relative roughness.

    (D)   The friction factor is independent of velocity.

504. A centrifugal pump provides 30 ft^3/min to a packed bed. The bed is 2 ft in diameter and contains a packing of 4-mm-diameter spherical particles with a bed porosity of 32%. The fluid has a density, ρ of 62.4 lb/ft^3, and viscosity, μ of 1 cP.

The Reynolds number for a packed bed is calculated as Re $= 4\,r_H u_b \rho/\mu$

where r_H = hydraulic radius = void volume of bed/surface area of packing
u_b = average interstitial velocity

The Reynolds number for the flow through the packed bed is most nearly:

(A)   60
(B)   190
(C)   387
(D)   406

505. A steam condensate stream at 30 psig contains 3% vapor by weight. If the piping specification allows for 15 ft/sec liquid or 100 ft/sec vapor, the minimum nominal line size of Sch. 40 pipe (in.) that should be chosen for a flow of 90,000 lb/hr is most nearly:

(A)   3
(B)   4
(C)   6
(D)   8

506. A salt-well cavity is 1,000 ft below grade. The cavity is filled with sodium chloride brine at 60°F. The well casing is 6-in. Sch. 40 pipe. There is an inner tube of 3-in. O.D. × 3/16-in. wall. Water at 70°F is pumped into the cavity through the annular space, displacing the brine and forcing it to surface through the inner tube into a storage tank. The brine discharge rate is 50 gpm. If the total friction head is 25 ft of water and the net static head ($h_2 - h_1$) is 225 ft of water, the pump power (hp) needed to transfer 50 gpm of brine is most nearly:

(A)   1.34
(B)   2.53
(C)   3.16
(D)   10.5

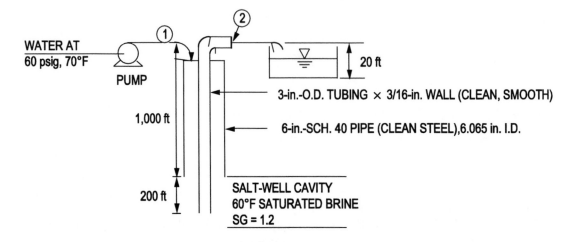

507. A horizontal piping system with both flows discharging to the atmosphere is shown in the figure. Both Fanning friction factors are approximately equal. The relationship between the velocities in Pipes 1 and 2 is most nearly:

(A) $v_2 = 0.78 \, v_1$

(B) $v_2 = 1.15 \, v_1$

(C) $v_2 = 1.28 \, v_1$

(D) $v_2 = 1.64 \, v_1$

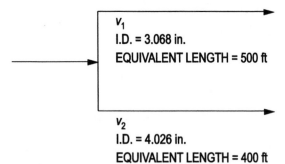

508. A centrifugal pump has a 9 1/2-in. impeller and moves 50 gal/min of 15 wt% sulfuric acid (sp gr = 1.10). The pump power (bhp) requirement is most nearly:

(A) 1.1
(B) 3.5
(C) 3.9
(D) 8.2

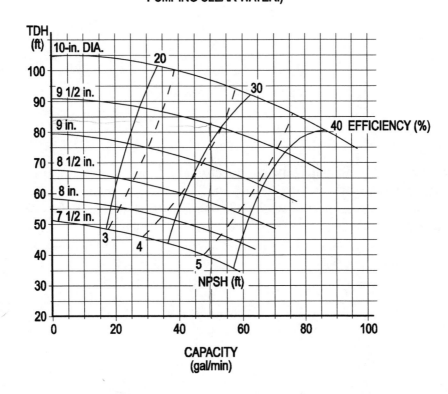

PUMP PERFORMANCE
CHARACTERISTICS

(CURVES SHOW APPROXIMATE
CHARACTERISTICS WHEN
PUMPING CLEAR WATER.)

509. A pump supplies water at a flow rate of 4.0 ft³/sec from an open reservoir through a horizontal 8-in. Sch. 40 suction pipe. The head loss from the reservoir to the suction of the pump is 2 ft-lbf/lbm, and the discharge is at 90 psig into a 6-in. Sch. 80 pipe (I.D. = 5.761 in.). The pump has an efficiency of 65%. The head (ft-lbf/lbm) that must be delivered by the pump to the water is most nearly:

(A) 207
(B) 217
(C) 251
(D) 334

510. A shell-and-tube heat exchanger uses cooling water in the tubes. There are two pressure gages installed on the water side of the heat exchanger. Gage 1 (P_1) is installed on the inlet water line, which is connected to the lower nozzle, while Gage 2 (P_2) is installed on the discharge water line, which is connected to the upper nozzle. Both pressure gages are very near the nozzle flanges. The pressure drop from each pressure gage to the exchanger channel is 1 psi. The vertical distance between the two pressure gages is 4'-8". The current pressure difference in tube-side pressure drop ($P_1 - P_2$) is 6 psi. If the number of tube passes were changed from 2 to 4 (with no appreciable change in the exchanger tube count), the water side pressure drop $P_1 - P_2$ (psi) would be most nearly:

(A)   12
(B)   20
(C)   28
(D)   34

511. An orifice meter with standard pipe tap locations is used to measure the flow of a liquid in a 4-in.-I.D. pipe. The orifice diameter is 1.6 in. A mercury (density = 848.6 lb/ft^3) manometer is used to measure the pressure differential across the orifice meter. Water (density = 62.4 lb/ft^3) is used in the legs of the manometer above the mercury surface as the sealing liquid. The reading of the manometer is 24 in. Assuming turbulent flow, the permanent pressure loss (psi) across the orifice meter is most nearly:

(A)   9.2
(B)   10.0
(C)   10.9
(D)   11.8

512. Either an orifice or a venturi can be used for the measurement of the flow in a pipe. For equal throat diameters, which of the following is true?

(A)   The flow rates for the same measured pressure drop are identical.

(B)   The orifice is more expensive.

(C)   The permanent pressure drop is less for a venturi.

(D)   The coefficients of discharge will be equal since the pipe and throat diameters are the same.

513. A cup and bob viscometer is used to measure the viscosity of a fluid. A "bob" is inserted into a "cup" containing the fluid to be measured. The bob spins inside the stationary cup, and a torque reading is displayed on the instrument. The bob radius is 2 cm, and the cup radius is 2.05 cm. The cup and bob are both 10 cm long. For a Newtonian liquid, a torque of 7,500 dyne·cm is measured at 10 rpm. The shear stress τ (dyne/cm^2) can be estimated by:

$$\tau = \frac{\Gamma}{2\pi r^2 L} = \mu \frac{dv}{dr}$$

where:

Γ = torque (dyne·cm)
r = bob radius (cm)
L = cup and bob length (cm)

The viscosity (dyne·sec/cm^2) is most nearly:

(A) 0.7
(B) 1.4
(C) 3.0
(D) 9.0

514. The Henry's law constant for carbon dioxide in seawater at 25°C is 35.4 atm/(mol/kg). This constant is based on concentration rather than activity in the liquid phase. For a CO_2 partial pressure of 0.000354 atm, the equilibrium concentration (mol/kg) of CO_2(aq) is most nearly:

(A) 0.000010
(B) 0.000354
(C) 0.0125
(D) 35.2

515. A chemical process separates a vapor-liquid mixture of 2-propanol and water at 176°F. At the operating conditions of the separation process, 2-propanol and water form an azeotropic mixture. The vapor pressure of 2-propanol is given by:

$$\ln P^{\text{sat}} = 8.8 - \frac{1,311.86}{t + 33.06}$$

where: P^{sat} = vapor pressure (psia)

t = temperature (°F)

The activity coefficient of 2-propanol in the azeotropic mixture is 1.08. The total pressure (atm) of the separation process is most nearly:

(A)   0.92
(B)   2.73
(C)   6.74
(D)   13.5

516. A mixture of vinyl acetate (nbp: 346 K), acetic acid (nbp: 391 K), and water is distilled in a continuous compound multitray column. Computer simulation results are shown in the figure superimposed on a mole fraction L-L phase diagram. The composition (mole fractions) of the aqueous distillate product is most nearly:

	Vinyl acetate	**Acetic acid**	**Water**
(A)	0.87	0.03	0.10
(B)	0.73	0.00	0.27
(C)	0.52	0.13	0.35
(D)	0.10	0.06	0.84

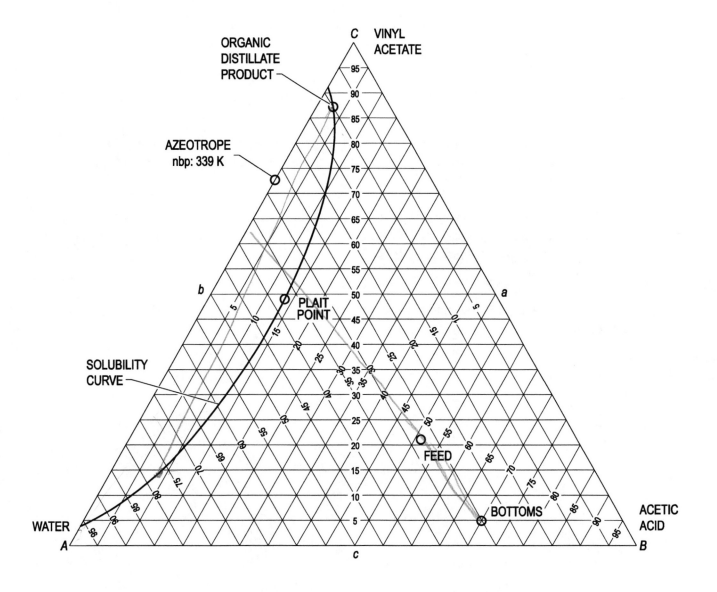

517. For a mixture of hydrocarbons ranging from ethane to heptane, which of the following actions will lower the dew-point temperature of the mixture?

(A)   Increasing the ethane concentration

(B)   Increasing the heptane concentration

(C)   Increasing the pressure

(D)   Increasing the temperature

518. Samples taken from a distillation column with a kettle reboiler yield the following mole fractions for one of the components:

Vapor from the bottom tray	0.70
Vapor from the reboiler	0.75
Liquid from the bottom tray	0.90
Bottom product	0.95

The ratio of the liquid flow rate from the bottom tray to the vapor flow rate from the reboiler is most nearly:

(A)   1.2
(B)   1.4
(C)   4.0
(D)   5.0

CHEMICAL PM PRACTICE EXAM

519. A gas absorber is used to reduce the carbon dioxide content of a gas through contact with an aqueous diethanolamine solution. The following results are obtained:

Pressure of operation, atm	0.967
Molecular weight of solvent, lb/lb mole	24
Entering liquid rate, lb/(sec-ft^2)	0.684
Equilibrium partial pressure of CO_2:	
for entering liquid, atm	0
for exiting liquid, atm	0.0658
Entering gas rate, lb mole/(sec-ft^2)	0.00181
CO_2 in entering gas, vol%	13.0
CO_2 in exiting gas, vol%	8.0

The CO_2 concentration (mole fraction) in the exit liquid is most nearly:

- (A)   0.000144
- (B)   0.00317
- (C)   0.00344
- (D)   0.0680

520. For a distillation column, which of the following tray designs provides the greatest turndown ratio?

- (A)   Single-pass sieve tray
- (B)   Two-pass sieve tray
- (C)   Single-pass valve tray
- (D)   Single-pass bubble-cap tray

521. The McCabe-Thiele diagram for a binary distillation column with a total condenser, partial reboiler, and 20 actual trays is shown in the figure. For the more volatile component, the feed has a mole fraction of 0.40 with a bottoms product of 0.03 and an overhead product of 0.80. With reflux at its bubble point, the minimum external reflux ratio is most nearly:

(A) 3.2
(B) 1.5
(C) 1.0
(D) 0.60

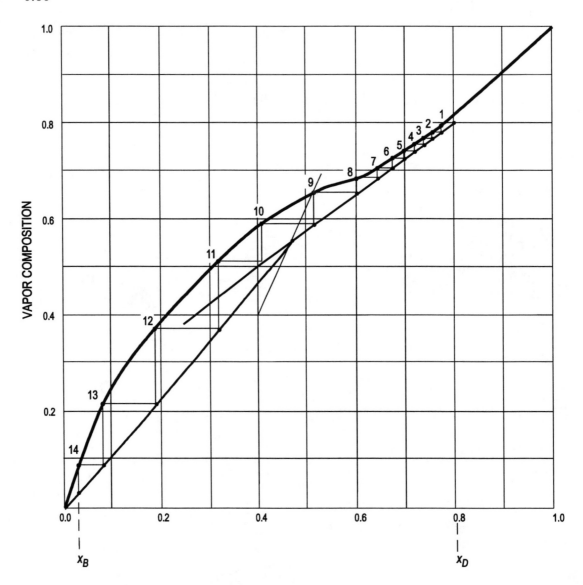

GO ON TO THE NEXT PAGE

522. Operating conditions for a column used to strip dissolved oxygen and nitrogen from liquid nitrous oxide are shown in the figure. The oxygen mole fractions are as follows:

	Top of the Packed Section	Bottom of the Packed Section
y	0.01	0.0000151
x	0.002	0.00000358

The Henry's law constant for oxygen is 5,000 psia. Ignore fugacity corrections. The number of liquid-phase transfer units (NTU_{oxygen}) required for the oxygen separation in the column packing is most nearly:

(A)　1.6
(B)　2.6
(C)　4.5
(D)　8.2

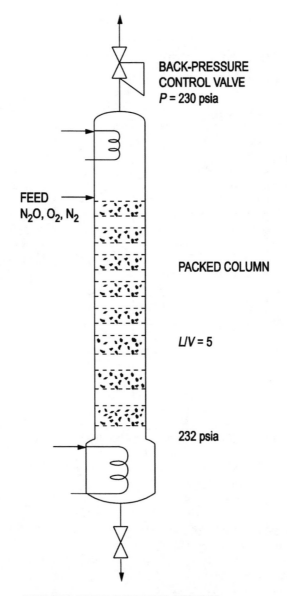

NITROUS OXIDE STRIPPING COLUMN

523. A packed tower is to be used to remove acetone from an air stream with pure water. The gas flow rate is 8.34 lb/sec. The following data apply:

Gas density	0.0909 lb/ft^3
Liquid density	62.4 lb/ft^3
Liquid viscosity	1.11 cP

One-inch plastic super Intalox packing ($F_p = 32 \text{ ft}^{-1}$) is selected for the column. The design is for a pressure drop of 1.0 in. of water per foot of packing. A generalized flooding and pressure-drop correlation is provided. For a water flow rate of 10.35 lb/sec, the column diameter (ft) is most nearly:

(A) 3.5
(B) 3.9
(C) 4.4
(D) 6.1

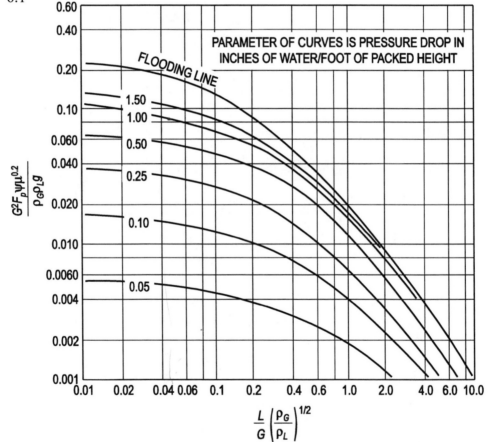

GENERALIZED FLOODING AND PRESSURE-DROP CORRELATION FOR PACKINGS

Original work by J.S.Eckert, *Chemical Engineering Progress*, American Institute of Chemical Engineers, 66(3):39, 1970.
Reproduced in Perry and Green, *Perry's Chemical Engineers' Handbook*, 6th ed., McGraw-Hill, 1984, p. 18-22. Used with permission.

524. Hydrogen sulfide (H_2S) is removed from an air stream by adsorption using granular activated carbon (GAC) in a fixed bed. The fixed bed contains 7,100 lb of GAC, which can be regenerated in 12 hours to a level of 0.0005 lb H_2S/lb GAC.

The adsorption isotherm is as follows:

$$Y^* = 855 \, X^* + 0.05$$

where:
Y^* = equilibrium concentration of H_2S on the GAC, lb H_2S/lb GAC
X^* = equilibrium concentration of H_2S in the air, lb H_2S/lb air

The flow of air is 10,000 lb/hr on an H_2S-free basis, and the air contains 0.001 lb H_2S/lb air. The time (hours) it will take to fully saturate the bed if the maximum H_2S concentration in the air discharge must be less than 2×10^{-6} lb H_2S/lb air is most nearly:

(A) 12
(B) 37
(C) 340
(D) 640

525. A food-processing plant is considering use of new gas-fired ovens with a total capital cost of $900,000, a useful life of 5 years, and a salvage value of $100,000. Using a net cash flow of $400,000/year for 5 years and a 7% discount rate, the net present value is most nearly:

(A) $1,640,000
(B) $811,000
(C) $787,000
(D) $740,000

526. Using ISA symbology, what is the correct way to represent an in-line pH meter with local display?

(A)

(B)

(C)

(D)

527. An ammonia-water stream (essentially at its bubble point) is processed in a trayed stripping column with a kettle reboiler to recover the majority of the ammonia. A constant molal overflow simulation provides the following information:

Number of theoretical stages	4.3
Overall tray efficiency	45%

If the tray spacing is 36 in., the height above the top tray is one tray spacing, and the height below the bottom tray is two tray spacings, the straight-side vessel height (ft) for the stripper column would be in the range of:

(A) 18–22
(B) 23–27
(C) 28–32
(D) 33–37

528. An ammonia-water stream (essentially at its bubble point) is processed in a trayed stripping column with an external kettle reboiler to recover the majority of the ammonia. A constant molal overflow simulation provides the following information:

Overhead ammonia mole fraction	0.95
Bottoms ammonia mole fraction	0.01
Feed ammonia mole fraction	0.40

The reboiler boilup ratio (V/B) for these conditions is most nearly:

(A) 0.41
(B) 0.58
(C) 0.71
(D) 1.41

529. A reactor is to be installed at a manufacturing plant. For pressure relief due to a multiphase-runaway reaction, the P&ID indicates a rupture disk on the reactor with discharge noted as "vent to a safe location." Which of the following is most likely to be regarded as a "safe location" for the vent discharge?

(A) Grade level adjacent to reactor

(B) Blowdown tank vented to the flare

(C) Flare header

(D) Vertically 10 ft above the reactor

530. Consider the following:

    I. 8-ft-diameter × 40-ft-tall distillation column
    II. 8-ft × 8-ft × 6-ft-deep cooling tower basin
    III. 8-ft × 8-ft × 10-ft-tall electrical room
    IV. 3-ft-diameter × 6-ft-tall boiler steam drum

Which of the above are considered to be confined spaces and require special entry procedures?

(A) I, II only

(B) I, II, IV only

(C) I, IV only

(D) III, IV only

531. A 12-ft-high vented oil storage tank uses a bubble tube that discharges air 1 ft from the bottom of the tank to measure its level. With an oil specific gravity of 0.85, operating at isotropic conditions, the percent expansion of the bubbles when the tank is 80% full is most nearly:

(A) 21.5%

(B) 23.0%

(C) 25.0%

(D) 27.5%

532. Crude mint oil is to be distilled continuously to remove water and dimethylsulfide (DMS). A process instrumentation diagram (PID) for the separation is shown. The water is removed after phase separation in the accumulator, and the DMS is removed in the cryo trap. The stripping section operates at essentially constant composition. Using the signal from pressure transmitter PT-2, the pressure in the column is **best** controlled by adjusting the setting of the:

(A) refrigerant control valve V-3

(B) speed controller Z-4 on the vacuum pump

(C) steam control valve V-2

(D) air bleed control valve V-4

533. Nitric acid (50 wt%) is used in a process at 100°C and 1 atm. The following materials are being considered for the reactor:

    I.   Stainless steel 316
   II. Mild steel
  III. Copper

Which of these materials are suitable?

(A)   I only

(B)   III only

(C)   I, II only

(D)   II, III only

534. During general plant maintenance, a centrifugal pump is disassembled for inspection. Upon inspection, potentially damaging microscopic cracks are suspected on an open impeller. The best way to evaluate this in a reasonable time frame is:

(A)   ultrasonic measurements

(B)   radiography/X-ray

(C)   dye penetrant examination

(D)   sounding

535. A centrifugal pump with a 4 3/4-in. impeller is not pumping the required 2 gal/min of HF acid (sp gr = 1.2). In order to protect the seal of the pump, 1 gal/min of seal liquid (sp gr = 0.7) is used as seal flush and enters the eye of the pump. The pump suction pressure is 10 psig and pumps into a vessel at 15 psig, 10 ft above the discharge of the pump. Assuming the line head loss is 1 ft of fluid, motor horsepower is adequate, and the pump speed is maximum, what needs to be done to the pump to make it work?

(A) Change the impeller to 5 1/4-in. diameter.

(B) Change the impeller to 5 1/2-in. diameter.

(C) Change the impeller to 5 3/4-in. diameter.

(D) Change the pump as the current pump will not work.

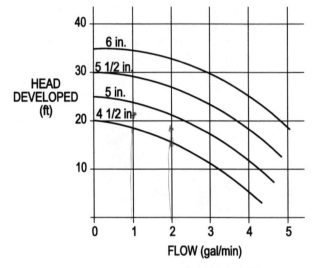

CENTRIFUGAL PUMP CURVE

536. Solid impurities are removed from a liquid product stream with a battery of bag filters. The flow rate diminishes with time as the filters become loaded according to the following equation and the figure.

$$y = 100\left(1 - e^{-(10 - 0.1x)}\right)$$

where

  y = percent of initial flow capability
  x = hours of operation subsequent to filter bag change

It requires 4 hours to remove used filter bags and install fresh bags. The total time (hours) between filter bag replacements, including operating time and outage time for filter bag replacement, that will result in the highest annual product throughput is most nearly:

(A) 50
(B) 72
(C) 76
(D) 104

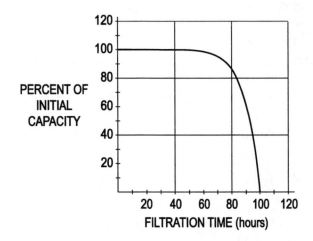

537. A tank farm occupies a square site, 100 ft on each side. The farm contains four tanks, each 30 ft in diameter and 30 ft in height. To provide the capacity required in the event of a failure of the largest tank, without an allowance for precipitation, the minimum height (ft) of a vertical containment dike around the site is most nearly:

(A) 2.12
(B) 2.69
(C) 2.96
(D) 8.48

538. A vessel containing 2 kg of toluene [MW = 92; R = 8.205 × 10^{-5} atm·m^3/(gm mole·K)] is left open in a 10-m × 10-m × 3-m room at 18.4°C. The saturation pressure of toluene at 18.4°C is 20 mm Hg. The maximum concentration of toluene (ppmv) in the room is most nearly:

    (A)   1,800
    (B)   6,600
    (C)   26,000
    (D)   27,000

539. An organic compound is produced in a vented, stirred steel reactor whose temperature is bounded by evaporation of hexane solvent (atmospheric boiling point is 156°F). The reactor is protected by a relief valve sized for an elementary first-order reaction occurring in the vessel.

The reactor is normally charged around 7:00 a.m. and the reaction is completed by mid-afternoon. One day the reactor did not get charged until 1:00 p.m., and the operator left it running overnight, thinking the reaction was nearly completed. Before leaving at 7:00 p.m., the operator closed the vent valve to prevent excessive solvent loss. At 8:00 p.m., the reactor exploded.

The most likely cause of the explosion was excessive reactor pressure because:

    (A)   the reaction was actually autocatalytic, so that increasing product concentration caused a rapid rate increase near the end of the reaction.

    (B)   heat generated by the stirrer increased the temperature enough to raise the hexane vapor pressure.

    (C)   the solvent level in the charge was too low causing the concentration, and thus the rate, to be higher than normal.

    (D)   the first-order reaction rate constant was actually higher than that used to size the relief valve.

540. Which of the following provides regulations regarding the treatment, storage, and disposal of hazardous wastes?

    (A)   Clean Air Act

    (B)   Occupational Health and Safety Act

    (C)   National Pollution Discharge Elimination System

    (D)   Resource Conservation and Recovery Act

This completes the afternoon session. Solutions begin on page 79.

Answers to the Chemical AM Practice Exam

Detailed solutions to each question begin on the next page.

101	A	121	B
102	A	122	B
103	B	123	A
104	B	124	D
105	A	125	B
106	C	126	B
107	C	127	B
108	C	128	D
109	D	129	B
110	B	130	A
111	D	131	C
112	B	132	A
113	D	133	C
114	D	134	B
115	B	135	B
116	D	136	C
117	B	137	B
118	C	138	C
119	B	139	A
120	C	140	A

CHEMICAL AM SOLUTIONS

101. Since the heating value given is on a dry and ash-free basis, first calculate the amount of organics in 1 lb of feed:

Without emulsifying agent: $1 \text{ lb} - (15\% \times 1 \text{ lb}) = 0.85 \text{ lb orimulsion}$

Amount of organics in orimulsion: 77%

$$0.85 \text{ lb} \times 0.77\% = 0.655 \text{ lb}$$

Calculate heating value: $\dfrac{0.655 \text{ lb organics}}{\text{lb feed}} \times \dfrac{16,800 \text{ Btu}}{\text{lb organics}} = 10,996 \text{ Btu/lb feed}$

THE CORRECT ANSWER IS (A)

102. The Clausius-Clapeyron equation describes the interdependence of pressure and temperature for a phase change:

$$\frac{dp}{dT} = \frac{\Delta H}{T \Delta V}$$

where

     ΔH is the heat of fusion
     T is the absolute temperature
     ΔV is the volume change on melting

T is always positive (absolute temperature).
ΔH is always positive (heat is required to melt a solid).

Thus ΔV must be negative to obtain a negative slope (dp/dT). The volume decreases as the solid melts, which means that the density of the solid is less than that of the liquid.

THE CORRECT ANSWER IS (A)

103. To calculate the flow rate of N_2 (lb/hr), first calculate the flow rate of N_2 (moles/hr) then convert to mass:

Flow rate of N_2: $100 \text{ lb moles/hr} \times 80 \text{ mol\%} = 80 \text{ lb moles } N_2\text{/hr}$

Mass flow rate of N_2: $80 \text{ lb moles/hr} \times 28 \text{ lb/lb moles} = 2,240 \text{ lb/hr}$

THE CORRECT ANSWER IS (B)

104. Perform a mass balance for water and KNO3 around the dissolver (do not include NaCl). Let D be the stream leaving the dissolver and R be the recycle stream:

$$D = R + 99 \text{ lb KNO}_3/\text{min} + 33.6 \text{ lb H}_2\text{O}/\text{min}$$

$$D = R + 132.6 \text{ lb/min}$$

Perform a KNO3 balance around the dissolver:

$$X_{\text{KNO}_3\,D} \times D = 99 \text{ lb KNO}_3/\text{min} + X_{\text{KNO}_3\,R} \times R$$

where $X_{\text{KNO}_3\,D}$ is the mass fraction of KNO3 leaving the dissolver, which is determined by the solubility:

$$X_{\text{KNO}_3\,D} = 138 \text{ lb KNO}_3/(138 \text{ lb KNO}_3 + 100 \text{ lb H}_2\text{O}) = 0.5798$$

and $X_{\text{KNO}_3\,R}$ is the mass fraction of X_{KNO_3} in the recycle, which has the same composition as the purge:

$$X_{\text{KNO}_3\,R} = 15.4 \text{ lb KNO}_3/(15.4 \text{ lb KNO}_3 + 33.6 \text{ lb H}_2\text{O}) = 0.3141$$

Combining the equations:

$$X_{\text{KNO}_3\,D}\,(R + 132.6 \text{ lb/min}) = 99 \text{ lb/min} + X_{\text{KNO}_3} \times R$$

Solving for R:

$$R = \frac{99 \text{ lb/min} - X_{\text{KNO}_3\,D} \times 132.6 \text{ lb/min}}{X_{\text{KNO}_3\,D} - X_{\text{KNO}_3\,R}}$$

$$= \frac{99 \text{ lb/min} - 76.88 \text{ lb/min}}{(0.5798 - 0.3141)}$$

$$= 83.25 \text{ lb/min}$$

THE CORRECT ANSWER IS (B)

105. Perform a mass balance around the reboiler:

$$L = V + B$$

Use B from table:

$$B = 1.259 \text{ lb mole/hr}$$

Use L/V ratio:

$$L = 1.4\,V$$

$$1.4\,V = V + 1.259 \text{ lb mole/hr}$$

$$V = \frac{1.259 \text{ lb mole/hr}}{0.4} = 3.15 \text{ lb mole/hr}$$

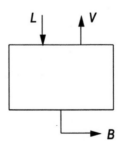

THE CORRECT ANSWER IS (A)

106. First, determine how much fuel was burned to produce 100 lb mole of dry flue gas (CO and CO_2 only). Since the ratio of carbon to hydrogen is given in weight %, calculate the fuel amount on a weight basis, not a mole basis.

Carbon in CO_2:

$$9.41 \text{ lb mole } CO_2 \times \frac{44 \text{ lb } CO_2}{\text{lb mole } CO_2} \times \frac{12 \text{ lb C}}{44 \text{ lb } CO_2} = 112.9 \text{ lb C}$$

Carbon in CO:

$$1.69 \text{ lb mole CO} \times \frac{28 \text{ lb CO}}{\text{lb mole CO}} \times \frac{12 \text{ lb C}}{28 \text{ lb CO}} = 20.3 \text{ lb C}$$

Total carbon $= 112.9 + 20.3 = 133.2 \text{ lb}$

Total hydrogen $= 133.2 \text{ lb C} \times 20/80 = 33.3 \text{ lb H}$

To calculate the oxygen needed for complete combustion, convert the amounts of carbon and hydrogen in the fuel back to a mole basis, and use the stoichiometric coefficients for complete combustion.

$$C + O_2 \rightarrow CO_2$$
$$H_2 + 0.5\, O_2 \rightarrow H_2O$$

Carbon:

$$133.2 \text{ lb C} \times \frac{\text{lb mole C}}{12 \text{ lb C}} \times \frac{1 \text{ lb mole } O_2}{1 \text{ lb mole C}} = 11.1 \text{ lb mole } O_2$$

Hydrogen:

$$33.3 \text{ lb H} \times \frac{\text{lb mole H}}{1 \text{ lb H}} \times \frac{1 \text{ lb mole } O_2}{4 \text{ lb mole H}} = 8.3 \text{ lb mole } O_2$$

Total oxygen needed $= 11.1 + 8.3 = 19.4 \text{ lb mole } O_2$

THE CORRECT ANSWER IS (C)

107. To calculate the single-pass conversion, first calculate the flow rate of MCB through the reactor and the amount of MCB consumed in the reactor:

MCB consumed:

    All fresh feed is converted to DCB or TCB (from balance around the whole system).

    Assume a basis of 1,000 lb mole/hr fresh feed.

MCB flow to reactor:

    Fresh feed and recycle flow (from given ratio)

    $= 1,000 \text{ lb MCB/hr} + 0.9 \times 1,000 \text{ lb MCB/hr} = 1,900 \text{ lb/hr}$

$$\text{Conversion} = \frac{\text{MCB consumed}}{\text{MCB flow to reactor}} = \frac{1,000 \text{ lb mole/hr}}{1,900 \text{ lb mole/hr}} \times 100\% = 52.6\%$$

THE CORRECT ANSWER IS (C)

108. To calculate the fresh feed rate of H_2S, first calculate the fresh feed rate of methanol and then use the information that the feed contains stoichiometric amounts.

Convert mass flow of mercaptan product to moles:

$$\frac{1,000 \text{ lb/hr}}{48.1 \text{ lb/lb mole}} = 20.79 \text{ lb mole/hr } CH_3SH$$

Use selectivity to calculate methanol feed:

$$\frac{20.79 \text{ lb mole/hr}}{0.90} = 23.1 \text{ lb mole/hr } CH_3OH$$

Based on the given reaction, the ratio of stoichiometric amounts of CH_3OH and H_2S is 1:1.

H_2S required $= 23.1$ lb mole/hr

THE CORRECT ANSWER IS (C)

109. Find the initial point on the pressure-enthalpy diagram by following the temperature line ($T = 150°C$) until it intersects with the constant pressure line (horizontal line) at 20 MPa. This is Point 1 indicated on the chart. The refrigerant has an enthalpy of 420 kJ/kg and a specific volume of 0.0011 m³/kg. Since the container is rigid, follow the constant volume line (down and left) until it intersects with the constant pressure line (horizontal) at 3.5 MPa. This is the final state marked as Point 2 on the chart. This point is to the left of the saturated liquid line on the diagram. Therefore, the refrigerant is a subcooled liquid.

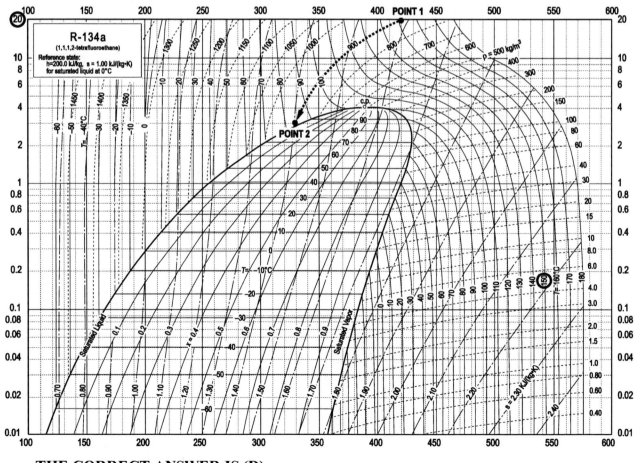

THE CORRECT ANSWER IS (D)

110. Calculate cooling water flow rate given the heat duty and temperature limits:

$$Q = 480,000 \text{ Btu/hr}$$
$$c_p = 1.0 \text{ Btu/(lb-F)}$$
$$T_{in} = 45°F$$
$$T_{out} = 110°F$$

$$Q = w c_p \Delta T \qquad \therefore w = \frac{Q}{c_p \Delta T}$$

$$w = \frac{480,000 \text{ Btu/hr}}{1 \text{ Btu/lbf } (110 - 45)}$$
$$= 7,385 \text{ lb/hr}$$

THE CORRECT ANSWER IS (B)

111. Feed:

From figure, enthalpy of pure water at 77°F is 42 Btu/lbm and enthalpy of pure H_2SO_4 is 5 Btu/lbm.

Water: $50 \text{ lb} \times \dfrac{42 \text{ Btu}}{\text{lbm}} = 2,250 \text{ Btu}$

Acid: $100 \text{ lb} \times \dfrac{5 \text{ Btu}}{\text{lbm}} = 500 \text{ Btu}$

Total $= 2,750 \text{ Btu}$

Product:

From figure, enthalpy of 0.67 wt fraction H_2SO_4 at 77°F is -125 Btu/lbm.

Mixture $= 150 \text{ lb} \times \dfrac{-125 \text{ Btu}}{\text{lbm}} = -18,750 \text{ Btu}$

Heat evolved:

$$Q = Q_{product} - Q_{feed} = -18,750 - 2,750 = -21,500 \text{ Btu}$$

This is the amount of heat that must be removed.

THE CORRECT ANSWER IS (D)

112. Enthalpy of dry air entering the dryer:

$$H_{DA} = \frac{1,000 \text{ kg}}{\text{s}} \times \frac{0.99 \text{ kJ}}{\text{kg} \cdot \text{K}} \times (405 - 298)\text{K} = 105,930 \text{ kJ/s}$$

The enthalpy of the moisture in air entering the dryer consists of the sensible heat plus the evaporation.

Enthalpy of evaporation:

$$H_{vap} = \frac{1,000 \text{ kg DA}}{\text{s}} \times \frac{7 \text{ g water}}{\text{kg DA}} \times \frac{1 \text{ kg}}{1,000 \text{ g}} \times 2,442 \text{ kJ/kg} = 17,094 \text{ kJ/s}$$

Sensible heat:

$$H_{moisture} = \frac{1,000 \text{ kg DA}}{\text{s}} \times \frac{7 \text{ g water}}{\text{kg DA}} \times \frac{1 \text{ kg}}{1,000 \text{ g}} \times \frac{2.01 \text{ kJ}}{\text{kg} \cdot \text{k}} \times (405 - 298)\text{K} = 1,505 \text{ kJ/s}$$

Total:

$$H = 105,930 \text{ kJ/s} + 17,094 \text{ kJ/s} + 1,505 \text{ kJ/s} = 124,529 \text{ kJ/s} = 124.5 \text{ MJ/s}$$

THE CORRECT ANSWER IS (B)

113. The heat of vaporization is estimated using the Clausius-Clapeyron equation.

$$\frac{d(\ln P^\circ)}{dT} = \frac{\Delta H_V}{RT^2}$$

Integrating

$$\ln \frac{P_2^0}{P_1^0} = -\frac{\Delta H_V}{R}\left(\frac{1}{T_2} - \frac{1}{T_1}\right)$$

Use data for 69.3°F and 84.4°F since these temperatures bracket 77°F

$$\ln \frac{0.0789}{0.0526} = -\Delta H_V \frac{\text{lb mole-R}}{1.987 \text{ Btu}}\left(\frac{1}{(84.4 + 459.7)\text{R}} - \frac{1}{(69.3 + 459.7)\text{R}}\right)$$

$$\Delta H_V = \frac{(0.40547) \times (1.987)}{0.5246 \times 10^{-4}} \text{ Btu/lb mole} = 15,357 \text{ Btu/lb mole}$$

THE CORRECT ANSWER IS (D)

CHEMICAL AM SOLUTIONS

114. Perform an energy balance where the heat of reaction is used as sensible heat increase of the flow exiting the reactor.

$$Q_{reaction} = \frac{24,000 \text{ kg feed}}{hr} \times \frac{0.1 \text{ kg PO}}{1 \text{ kg feed}} \times \frac{0.8 \text{ kg PO converted}}{1 \text{ kg PO}} \times \frac{1,459 \text{ kJ}}{\text{kg PO converted}} = 2,801,280 \text{ kJ/hr}$$

$$Q_{reaction} = w\,c_p\,\Delta T = \frac{24,000 \text{ kg}}{hr} \times \frac{4.18 \text{ kJ}}{kg \times K} \times \Delta T = 2,801,280 \text{ kJ/hr}$$

$$\Delta T = \frac{2,801,280}{24,000 \times 4.18} = 27.9 \text{ K}$$

$$T_{effluent} = 20 + 27.9 = 47.9°C = 321 \text{ K}$$

THE CORRECT ANSWER IS (D)

115. Evaluate the standard heat of reaction:

$$NH_3 + (2.5/2)\,O_2(g) \rightarrow NO(g) + (3/2)\,H_2O(g)$$

Heats of formation:

$$NH_3(g) = -11.05 \text{ kcal/g mole}$$
$$NO(g) = 21.60 \text{ kcal/g mole}$$
$$H_2O(g) = -57.80 \text{ kcal/g mole}$$

$$(\Delta H^0_{298})_{rxn} = \sum (\Delta H^0_{298})_{products} - \sum (\Delta H^0_{298})_{reactants}$$

$$= \left[1 \times (\Delta H^0_{298})_{NO\,(g)} + (3/2) \times (\Delta H^0_{298})_{H_2O\,(g)} \right] -$$

$$\left[1 \times (\Delta H^0_{298})_{NH_3\,(g)} + (2.5/2) \times (\Delta H^0_{298})_{O_2\,(g)} \right]$$

$$= \left[1 \times 21.60 + (3/2) \times (-57.80) \right] - \left[1 \times (-11.05) + (2.5/2) \times 0 \right] \text{ kcal/g mole}$$

$$= -54.05 \frac{kcal}{g \text{ mole}} \times \frac{4.184 \text{ kJ}}{kcal} = -226.1 \text{ kJ/g mole}$$

THE CORRECT ANSWER IS (B)

116. Polymers have a molecular weight range distribution, not a unique value for the molecular weight. Thus, it is not possible to use the mole fraction, so the weight fraction is used instead. Vapor pressure of the polymer, viscosity, and density are not needed for equilibrium calculations for the solute.

THE CORRECT ANSWER IS (D)

CHEMICAL AM SOLUTIONS

117. Use the Mollier diagram below to determine the quality of steam leaving the turbine. Locate the point on the chart that corresponds to $p = 150$ psia and $T = 760°F$ (labeled 1). The turbine process is isentropic so follow the constant entropy line to where $p = 1.47$ psia (labeled 2). According to the chart this will be about 9% moisture or 91% quality $(1 - 0.09 = 0.91)$.

THE CORRECT ANSWER IS (B)

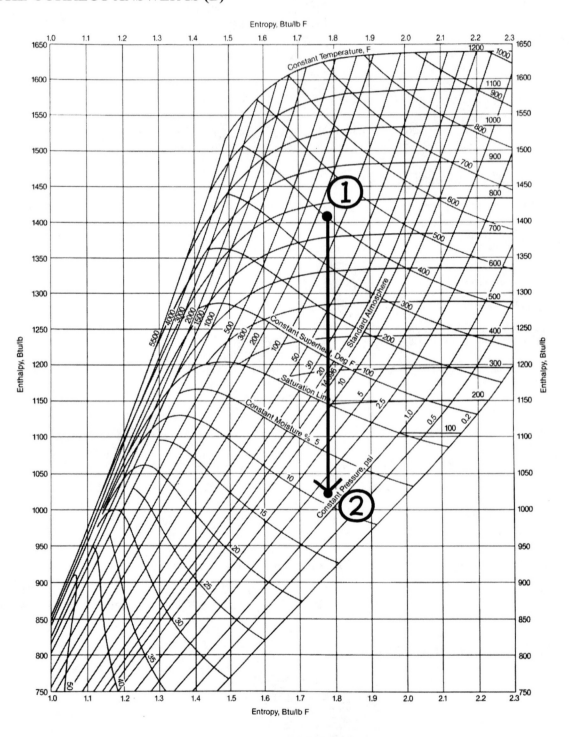

Courtesy of The Babcock & Wilcox Company.

118. For this system:

$$w_s = h_{in} - h_{out}$$
$$\Delta s = 0$$

From steam tables for superheated steam at 250 psia and 800°F:

$h_{in} = 1,422.75$ Btu/lb, $s_{in} = 1.7398$ Btu/(lb-R)

For the outlet stream (also from steam tables) for saturated steam at 2.89 psia:

$h_v = 1,122.0$ Btu/lb, $s_v = 1.8894$ Btu/(lb-R)
$h_l = 107.89$ Btu/lb, $s_l = 0.1984$ Btu/(lb-R)

Entropy is unchanged:

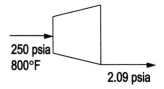

250 psia
800°F

2.09 psia

$$xs_v + (1-x)s_l = x(1.8894) + (1-x)(0.1984) = 1.7398$$

$$x = \frac{1.7398 - 0.1984}{1.8894 - 0.1984} = 0.91153$$

Enthalpy change is the work:

$$h_{out} = xh_v + (1-x)h_l$$
$$h_{out} = 0.91153 \times 1,122.0 + (1 - 0.91153) \times 107.89 = 1,032.28 \text{ Btu/lb}$$
$$w_s = h_{in} - h_{out}$$
$$w_s = 1,422.75 - 1,032.28 = 390.5 \text{ Btu/lb}$$

Hint: This problem can be solved more quickly using the Mollier diagram.

THE CORRECT ANSWER IS (C)

119. The heat flux q is calculated from the following equation:

$$q = \frac{Q}{A} = U \times \Delta T$$

For the comparison of a single- and double-pane window, the temperature differences between the inside and outside of the windows are the same, so the ratio of the heat flux is the same as the ratio of the heat transfer coefficients:

$$\frac{q_2}{q_1} = \frac{U_2}{U_1}$$

For the single-pane window, include inside convection, conduction through the window pane, and outside convection:

$$\frac{1}{U_1} = \frac{1}{h_i} + \frac{\Delta x_{glass}}{k_{glass}} + \frac{1}{h_o} = \frac{2}{h} + \frac{\Delta x_{glass}}{k_{glass}}$$

$$= \frac{2}{1\ Btu/(hr\text{-}ft^2\text{-}F)} + \frac{0.25\ in.}{0.5\ Btu/(hr\text{-}ft^2\text{-}F)} \times \frac{1\ ft}{12\ in.}$$

$$= 2.042\ hr\text{-}ft^2\text{-}F/Btu$$

For the double-pane window, additional terms for the second pane and the air gap need to be included:

$$\frac{1}{U_2} = \frac{1}{h_i} + \frac{\Delta x_{glass}}{k_{glass}} + \frac{\Delta x_{air}}{k_{air}} + \frac{\Delta x_{glass}}{k_{glass}} + \frac{1}{h_o} = \frac{2}{h} + \frac{2\Delta x_{glass}}{k_{glass}} + \frac{\Delta x_{air}}{k_{air}}$$

$$= \frac{2}{1\ Btu/(hr\text{-}ft^2\text{-}F)} + \frac{(2)(0.25\ in.)}{0.5\ Btu/(hr\text{-}ft^2\text{-}F)} \times \frac{1\ ft}{12\ in.} + \frac{(0.25\ in.)}{0.015\ Btu/(hr\text{-}ft^2\text{-}F)} \times \frac{1\ ft}{12\ in.}$$

$$= 3.4722\ hr\text{-}ft^2\text{-}F/Btu$$

Thus, the ratio of the heat fluxes is:

$$\frac{q_2}{q_1} = \frac{U_2}{U_1} = \frac{1/U_1}{1/U_2} = \frac{2.042\ hr\text{-}ft^2/Btu}{3.472\ hr\text{-}ft^2/Btu} = 0.588$$

THE CORRECT ANSWER IS (B)

120. The heat transfer through the insulation can be calculated from the interior and exterior wall temperatures using Fourier's Law. Since the wall temperatures are given, convection coefficients are not needed.

$$Q = \frac{kA_m}{\delta} \Delta T$$

where A_m is the mean area for heat transfer and δ is the thickness of the insulation. The furnace wall is cylindrical, thus A_m is calculated using the log mean diameter D_m:

$$A_m = H\pi D_m = H\pi \frac{D_o - D_i}{\ln(D_o/D_i)} \qquad \text{and} \qquad \delta = \frac{1}{2}(D_o - D_i)$$

where H is the height of the furnace, and D_i and D_o are the inner and outer diameters of the insulation.

$$\frac{A_m}{\delta} = \frac{2\pi H}{\ln(D_o/D_i)} \qquad \text{and} \qquad Q = \frac{k2\pi H}{\ln(D_o/D_i)} \Delta T$$

The following data apply:

$H = 12 \text{ ft}$

$D_i = 33 \text{ ft} + 4 \text{ in.} = 400 \text{ in.}$

$D_o = D_i + 2\delta = 400 \text{ in.} + 2 \times 30 \text{ in.} = 460 \text{ in.}$

$k = 1 \text{ Btu/(hr-ft-F)}$

$\Delta T = T_i - T_o = 1,200°F - 77°F = 1,123 \text{ F}$

The energy loss through the cylindrical furnace wall is thus:

$$Q = \frac{k2\pi H}{\ln(D_o/D_i)} \Delta T$$

$$Q = \frac{1 \text{ Btu(hr-ft-F)} \times 2 \times \pi \times 12 \text{ ft}}{\ln(460 \text{ in.}/400 \text{ in.})} \times 1,123 \text{ F} = 605,831 \text{ Btu/hr}$$

THE CORRECT ANSWER IS (C)

CHEMICAL AM SOLUTIONS

121. To calculate the heat transfer coefficient, first calculate the Nusselt number from the equation given:

$$N_{Re} = 3 \times 10^5$$

$$N_{Pr} = 0.9$$

$$N_{Nu} = 0.664 \times (N_{Re})^{0.5} \times (N_{Pr})^{0.33} = 0.664 \times (3 \times 10^5)^{0.5} \times (0.9)^{0.33} = 351.26$$

Then, use the definition of the Nusselt number and solve for the heat transfer coefficient:

$$N_{Nu} = \frac{h \times L}{k} \qquad h = \frac{N_{Nu} \times k}{L}$$

$$h = \frac{351.26 \times 0.0156 \text{ Btu/(hr-ft}^2\text{-F)}}{1 \text{ ft}} = 5.47 \text{ Btu/(hr-ft-F)}$$

THE CORRECT ANSWER IS (B)

122. The heat flux can be calculated using Fourier's Law and the overall heat transfer coefficient. Since the diameter is large compared to the wall thickness, the one-dimensional form can be used:

$$q = \frac{Q}{A} = U_o \Delta T$$

The overall heat transfer coefficient includes convective heat transfer from the fluid to the wall, the effects of fouling, the conductive heat transfer through the tank wall, and the convective heat transfer from the tank wall to the surroundings:

$$\frac{1}{U_o} = \frac{1}{h_i} + r_{\text{fouling}} + \frac{\delta_{\text{wall}}}{k_{\text{wall}}} + \frac{1}{h_i}$$

$$\frac{1}{U_o} = \frac{1}{30 \text{ Btu/(hr-ft}^2\text{-F)}} + 0.010 \text{ hr-ft}^2\text{-F/Btu} + \frac{1.5 \text{ in.}(1 \text{ ft/12 in.})}{23 \text{ Btu/(hr-ft-F)}} + \frac{1}{10 \text{ Btu/(hr-ft}^2\text{-F)}}$$

$$\frac{1}{U_o} = (0.033 + 0.010 + 0.005 + 0.100) \text{ hr-ft}^2\text{-F/Btu} = 0.148 \text{ hr-ft}^2\text{-F/Btu}$$

The temperature difference is $\Delta T = T_i - T_o = 190°\text{F} - (-20°\text{F}) = 210°\text{F}$.

The heat flux to the surroundings is $q = \dfrac{\Delta T}{1/U_o} = \dfrac{210°\text{F}}{0.148 \text{ hr-ft}^2\text{-F/Btu}} = 1,419 \text{ Btu/(hr-ft}^2)$.

THE CORRECT ANSWER IS (B)

123. The first step is to perform an energy balance around a unit area (A) of the roof. Since the roof has reached equilibrium (steady state) temperature, there is no energy accumulation. There is also no energy generation within the roof. The energy balance thus states that the heat input from solar radiation is equal to the heat transferred from the roof to the surroundings.

Heat input:

$$q_{in} = \frac{Q}{A} = \varepsilon_{ad,sol} \times q_{sol} = 0.8 \times 300 \ Btu/(hr\text{-}ft^2) = 240 \ Btu/(hr\text{-}ft^2)$$

The heat output from the roof to the surroundings occurs by convection and radiation:

Convection:

$$q_{conv} = \left[0.38 \ Btu/(hr\text{-}ft^2)\right]\left(\frac{\Delta T}{F}\right)^{1.25} = \left[0.38 \ Btu/(hr\text{-}ft^2)\right]\left(\frac{T_{roof} - T_{air}}{F}\right)^{1.25}$$

$$q_{conv} = \left[0.38 \ Btu/(hr\text{-}ft^2)\right]\left(\frac{177.5°F - 80°F}{F}\right)^{1.25} = (0.38)(97.5)^{1.25} \ Btu/(hr\text{-}ft^2) = 116 \ Btu/(hr\text{-}ft^2)$$

From the energy balance:

$$q_{in} = q_{conv} + q_{rad}$$

$$q_{rad} = q_{in} - q_{conv} = 240 \ Btu/(hr\text{-}ft^2) - 116 \ Btu/(hr\text{-}ft^2) = 124 \ Btu/(hr\text{-}ft^2)$$

Radiative heat flux as a percentage of total heat flux:

$$\frac{q_{rad}}{q_{in}} = \frac{124 \ Btu/(hr\text{-}ft^2)}{240 \ Btu/(hr\text{-}ft^2)} = 0.517 = 51.7\%$$

THE CORRECT ANSWER IS (A)

124. Typically, heat transfer increases with increasing temperature differential (i.e., the driving force for heat transfer). However, in boiling heat transfer, the formation of a vapor film next to the heat transfer surface impedes heat transfer and leads to a decrease in heat transfer with increasing temperature difference as the transition from nucleate to film boiling occurs.

From the given options for the heat transfer curves, only Option D exhibits such a local maximum (corresponding to nucleate boiling) with a subsequent drop in heat transfer at the onset of film boiling. Once film boiling is well established, the heat transfer increases again with increasing temperature difference.

THE CORRECT ANSWER IS (D)

125. Since the steam generated from the feedwater exits the exchanger as saturated steam at 440°F, the vaporization occurs at 440°F. The incoming liquid is first heated to the boiling point (sensible heat) and then vaporized (latent heat).

The sensible heat (i.e., the heat required to heat the liquid to the boiling point) is the difference in enthalpy between the liquid at saturation (440°F) and the subcooled liquid at feed conditions (120°F):

$$\Delta h_{\text{sensible}} = h_{L,400°F} - h_{L,120°F} = 419 \text{ Btu/lb} - 89 \text{ Btu/lb} = 330 \text{ Btu/lb}$$

The total heat transferred to the feedwater in the exchanger is the difference in enthalpy between the vapor at saturation (outlet condition) and the subcooled liquid feedwater at 120°F (inlet condition):

$$\Delta h_{\text{total}} = H_{V,400°F} - h_{L,120°F} = 1{,}205 \text{ Btu/lb} - 89 \text{ Btu/lb} = 1{,}116 \text{ Btu/lb}$$

The sensible heat as a percentage of the total heat transferred is:

$$\frac{\Delta h_{\text{sensible}}}{\Delta h_{\text{total}}} = \frac{330 \text{ Btu/lb}}{1{,}116 \text{ Btu/lb}} = 29.6\%$$

THE CORRECT ANSWER IS (B)

126. To calculate the outlet temperature for the cooling water, use the equation for heat transfer in a heat exchanger:

$$Q = U_o A \Delta T_{log} = U_o A \frac{(T_{az} - T_{in}) - (T_{az} - T_{out})}{\ln(T_{az} - T_{in})/(T_{az} - T_{out})} = \frac{U_o A (T_{out} - T_{in})}{\ln(T_{az} - T_{in})/(T_{az} - T_{out})}$$

T_{az} is the temperature of the process stream (i.e., boiling temperature of the azeotrope). The heat duty of the exchanger (Q), the overall heat transfer coefficient (U_o), the area of the heat exchanger (A), and the cooling water inlet temperature (T_{in}) are given in the question statement. The only unknown in this equation is the outlet temperature of the cooling water (T_{out}).

However, T_{out} appears twice in this equation, once in the numerator and once in the logarithm. It is possible to solve for T_{out} iteratively, but a faster way is to check the given answers to see which one best satisfies the equation:

$$\frac{\left[155 \text{ Btu/(hr-ft}^2\text{-F)}\right](50 \text{ ft}^2)(T_{out} - 85°F)}{\ln(126.7°F - 85°F)/(126.7°F - T_{out})} = 282,500 \text{ Btu/hr}$$

(A) $T_{out} = 90°F \Rightarrow \dfrac{\left[155 \text{ Btu/(hr-ft}^2\text{-F)}\right](50 \text{ ft}^2)(90°F - 85°F)}{\ln(126.7°F - 85°F)/(126.7°F - 90°F)} = 303,388 \text{ Btu/hr}$

(B) $T_{out} = 95°F \Rightarrow \dfrac{\left[155 \text{ Btu/(hr-ft}^2\text{-F)}\right](50 \text{ ft}^2)(95°F - 85°F)}{\ln(126.7°F - 85°F)/(126.7°F - 95°F)} = 282,656 \text{ Btu/hr}$

(C) $T_{out} = 103°F \Rightarrow \dfrac{\left[155 \text{ Btu/(hr-ft}^2\text{-F)}\right](50 \text{ ft}^2)(103°F - 85°F)}{\ln(126.7°F - 85°F)/(126.7°F - 103°F)} = 246,891 \text{ Btu/hr}$

(D) $T_{out} = 118°F \Rightarrow \dfrac{\left[155 \text{ Btu/(hr-ft}^2\text{-F)}\right](50 \text{ ft}^2)(117°F - 85°F)}{\ln(126.7°F - 85°F)/(126.7°F - 117°F)} = 163,191 \text{ Btu/hr}$

Based on the calculated values, $T_{out} = 95°F$ results in a heat duty closest to the given heat duty.

THE CORRECT ANSWER IS (B)

127. The length of the worm heater determines the area available for heat transfer. It has to be calculated such that the amount of heat transferred (for the given values of temperature and heat transfer coefficient) equals the amount of heat lost to the surroundings.

$$Q = U_o A \Delta T = U_o \pi D_{\text{outer}} L \Delta T$$

It is not necessary to use the log mean temperature difference, since both the tank temperature and the temperature of the condensing steam are constant. The temperature of the saturated steam (from steam tables at 50 psig) is:

$$T_{\text{steam}} (50 \text{ psig}) = 298°F$$

$$\Delta T = T_{\text{steam}} - T_{\text{tank}} = 298°F - 250°F = 48°F$$

The overall heat transfer coefficient is:

$$\frac{1}{U_o} = \frac{1}{h_{\text{outer}}} + \frac{D_{\text{outer}}}{2k} \ln\left(\frac{D_{\text{outer}}}{D_{\text{inner}}}\right) + \frac{D_{\text{outer}}}{D_{\text{inner}} \times h_{\text{outer}}}$$

$$= \frac{1}{40 \text{ Btu/(hr-ft}^2\text{-F)}} + \frac{1.315 \text{ in.}(1 \text{ ft/12 in.})}{2 \times 26 \text{ Btu/(hr-ft}^2\text{-F)}} \ln\left(\frac{1.315 \text{ in.}}{1.049 \text{ in.}}\right) + \frac{1.315 \text{ in.}}{1.049 \text{ in.} \times 1,200 \text{ Btu/(hr-ft}^2\text{-F)}}$$

$$= \left[(250 \times 10^{-4}) + (4.76 \times 10^{-4}) + (10.44 \times 10^{-4})\right] \text{hr-ft}^2\text{-F/Btu} = 265.2 \times 10^{-4} \text{ hr-ft}^2\text{-F/Btu}$$

$$U_o = 37.71 \text{ Btu/(hr-ft}^2\text{-F)}$$

The required length of the worm heater is:

$$L = \frac{Q}{U_o \pi D_{\text{outer}} \Delta T}$$

$$L = \frac{75,000 \text{ Btu/hr}}{\left[37.71 \text{ Btu/(hr-ft}^2\text{-F)}\right] \pi \, 1.315 \text{ in.}(1 \text{ ft/12 in.}) \, 48°F} = 120.36 \text{ ft}$$

THE CORRECT ANSWER IS (B)

128. In order to calculate the steam flow rate to the jacket, we need to know how much energy is needed to evaporate the water. With the information given in the question statement, the heat duty can be calculated from the heat transfer equation:

$$m_{steam}\Delta h_{vap(20\ psig)} = Q = U_o A \Delta T$$

The temperature in the jacket is the saturation temperature of 20-psig steam. The temperature in the evaporator is the saturation temperature of 0-psig (1-atm) steam. From the steam table:

$$T_{sat(0\ psig)} = 212°F$$

$$T_{sat(20\ psig)} = 259.3°F$$

$$\Delta h_{vap(20\ psig)} = 939.1\ Btu/lb$$

The heat transferred in the evaporator is:

$$Q = U_o A \Delta T = \left[400\ Btu/(hr\text{-}ft^2\text{-}F)\right](900\ ft^2)(259.3°F - 212°F) = 17.03 \times 10^6\ Btu/hr$$

The amount of steam necessary to supply this heat is:

$$m_{steam} = \frac{Q}{\Delta h_{vap\ (20\ psig)}} = \frac{17,028,000\ Btu/hr}{939.1\ Btu/lb} = 18,132\ lb/hr$$

THE CORRECT ANSWER IS (D)

129. The question statement asks for the outlet temperature at the minimum cooling water flow rate. Minimum water flow occurs when the temperatures of the two streams become equal at some point in the exchanger (pinch point). In this question, the temperature profile of the condensing ammonia is **not** linear (see figure supplied with the question statement), and thus the pinch point does not happen at the exit, but within the exchanger. The temperature of the ammonia first decreases as the superheated ammonia is cooled to the condensing temperature and then remains constant at 110°F as the ammonia condenses. The pinch point will occur where ammonia first starts to condense.

For the purpose of the calculations, the exchanger is analyzed in two sections—the cooling of the ammonia vapor and the constant temperature condensation of the ammonia vapor. The pinch point is where the two sections connect. The condensing section will be used to calculate the minimum water flow rate, and the cooling section will then be used to calculate the water outlet temperature.

The heat transferred in the condensing section is:

$$Q_{cond} = m_{ammonia} \left[H_{V(247 \text{ psig, } 110°F)} \right] - \left[h_{L(247 \text{ psig, } 110°F)} \right]$$

$$Q_{cond} = (17,250 \text{ lb/hr})(633.7 \text{ Btu/lb} - 167.0 \text{ Btu/lb}) = 8,050,575 \text{ Btu/hr}$$

The minimum water flow rate is obtained when the cooling water reaches 110°F at the point where the ammonia starts to condense:

$$m_{water} = \frac{Q_{cond}}{C_{p,w} \Delta T_w} = \frac{8,050,575 \text{ Btu/hr}}{[1 \text{ Btu/(lb-F)}](110°F - 80°F)} = 268,352.5 \text{ lb/hr}$$

The outlet temperature of the cooling water will be higher than 110°F since it will absorb the heat from the cooling section of the exchanger after the pinch point:

$$Q_{cool} = m_{ammonia} \left[H_{V(252 \text{ psig, } 250°F)} \right] - \left[H_{V(247 \text{ psig, } 110°F)} \right]$$

$$Q_{cool} = (17,250 \text{ lb/hr})(733.3 \text{ Btu/lb} - 633.7 \text{ Btu/lb}) = 1,718,100 \text{ Btu/hr}$$

The water at minimum flow rate enters the cooling section at 110°F. The exit temperature of the water is:

$$T_{w, out} = T_{w, in} + \frac{Q_{cool}}{m_{water} c_{p,w}} = 110°F + \frac{1,718,100 \text{ Btu/hr}}{(268,325.5 \text{ lb/hr})[1 \text{ Btu/(lb-F)}]} = 116.4°F$$

THE CORRECT ANSWER IS (B)

130. The question states that the reactor can be treated as a flat surface, and thus the heat flux (q) can be calculated from Fourier's Law for a slab:

$$q = \frac{Q}{A} = U_o \Delta T = U_o(T_{c-\text{layer}} - T_{\text{ambient}})$$

$$U_o = \frac{q}{\Delta T} = \frac{650 \text{ Btu/(hr-ft}^2)}{2{,}150°\text{F} - 75°\text{F}} = 0.31325 \text{ Btu/(hr-ft}^2\text{-F)}$$

The overall heat transfer coefficient is calculated from the heat transfer through the carbon laydown (fouling heat transfer coefficient), the heat transfer coefficient through the brick, the heat transfer through the steel shell, and the convective/radiation heat transfer coefficient:

$$\frac{1}{U_o} = \frac{1}{h_{\text{foul}}} + \frac{\delta_{\text{brick}}}{k_{\text{brick}}} + \frac{\delta_{\text{shell}}}{k_{\text{shell}}} + \frac{1}{h_o}$$

It is not necessary to include the inside convective/radiation heat transfer coefficient, since the temperature on the surface of the carbon layer is given, not the temperature inside the reactor. The equation above can be used to calculate the fouling heat transfer coefficient:

$$\frac{1}{h_{\text{foul}}} = \frac{1}{U_o} - \frac{\delta_{\text{brick}}}{k_{\text{brick}}} - \frac{\delta_{\text{shell}}}{k_{\text{shell}}} - \frac{1}{h_i}$$

$$\frac{1}{h_{\text{foul}}} = \frac{1}{0.31325 \text{ Btu/(hr-ft}^2\text{-F)}} - \frac{(6 \text{ in.})(1 \text{ ft/12 in.})}{8 \text{ Btu/(hr-ft-F)}} - \frac{(1.5 \text{ in.})(1 \text{ ft/12 in.})}{26 \text{ Btu/(hr-ft-F)}} - \frac{1}{1.5 \text{ Btu/(hr-ft}^2\text{-F)}}$$

$$\frac{1}{h_{\text{foul}}} = (3.1923 - 0.0625 - 0.0048 - 0.6667) \text{ hr-ft}^2\text{-F/Btu} = 2.4585 \text{ hr-ft}^2\text{-F/Btu}$$

$$h_{\text{foul}} = \frac{1}{1/h_{\text{foul}}} = \frac{1}{2.4585 \text{ hr-ft}^2\text{-F/Btu}} = 0.407 \text{ Btu/(hr-ft}^2\text{-F)}$$

THE CORRECT ANSWER IS (A)

131. If the molecular weight increases by 20% at constant volumetric flow, the mass flow rate will increase by 20%. This will result in a decrease in the change in temperature (ΔT) for the gas. The heat transfer coefficient on the gas side will also increase by $(1.2)^{0.8}$, but this is not sufficient to compensate for the increased mass flow rate. Thus, **the outlet temperature of the gas will increase**.

The increased outlet temperature of the gas results in a higher log mean temperature difference for the exchanger. This increase in driving force together with the increased heat transfer coefficient increases the heat duty of the exchanger. The cooling water absorbs more heat. At constant cooling water flow rate, **the outlet temperature of the cooling water will increase**.

THE CORRECT ANSWER IS (C)

CHEMICAL AM SOLUTIONS

132. Assuming Langmuir-Hinshelwood kinetics for adsorption of A on the catalyst surface:

At steady-state: $d\Theta/dt = k_1 P_A (1 - \Theta) - k_2 \Theta = 0$

where Θ = fraction of catalyst surface covered with adsorbed A.

Solving for Θ $\quad \Theta = KP_A/(1 + KP_A)$ $\quad$ where $K = k_1/k_2$

Also $\quad -dP_A/dt = k'\Theta P_B = k'K\, P_A P_B/(1 + KP_A)$

$\quad\quad\quad\quad\quad = kP_A P_B/(1 + KP_A)$

This form of rate expression could only result from assuming that the reaction is between gaseous reactant B and adsorbed reactant A on the catalyst surface.

THE CORRECT ANSWER IS (A)

133. Denote k_1 and k_2 as the forward and reverse rate constants for the first reaction and k_3 and k_4 as the rate constants for the second reaction of the proposed mechanism. For this mechanism to be valid, we must make the assumption of dynamic equilibrium for A*, which makes $r_{A*} = 0$.

$$r_{A*} = k_1 C_A - k_2 C_{A*} - k_3 C_{A*} C_B + k_4 C_{AB} = 0$$

Solving for C_{A*}:

$$C_{A*} = (k_1 C_A + k_4 C_{AB})/(k_2 + k_3 C_B)$$

The formation of AB is given by:

$$r_{AB} = k_3 C_{A*} C_B - k_4 C_{AB}$$

Substituting the above for C_{A*} gives:

$$r_{AB} = k_3 C_B (k_1 C_A + k_4 C_{AB})/(k_2 + k_3 C_B) - k_4 C_{AB}$$

Multiplying $k_4 C_{AB}$ by $(k_2 + k_3 C_B)/(k_2 + k_3 C_B)$ gives a common denominator:

$$r_{AB} = [k_3 C_B(k_1 C_A + k_4 C_{AB}) - k_4 C_{AB}(k_2 + k_3 C_B)]/(k_2 + k_3 C_B)$$

Multiplying through yields two terms that will cancel out:

$$r_{AB} = (k_1 k_3 C_A C_B + k_3 k_4 C_B C_{AB} - k_2 k_4 C_{AB} - k_3 k_4 C_{AB} C_B)/(k_2 + k_3 C_B)$$

So: $\quad r_{AB} = (k_1 k_3 C_A C_B - k_2 k_4 C_{AB})/(k_2 + k_3 C_B)$

However, it is assumed that k_4 is negligible relative to the other reactions, simplifying to:

$$r_{AB} = (k_1 k_3 C_A C_B)/(k_2 + k_3 C_B)$$

Dividing the numerator and denominator by k_2 yields the final form with constants a_1, a_2:

$$r_{AB} = a_1 C_A C_B/(1 + a_2 C_B) \quad\quad \text{(where } a_1 = k_1 k_3/k_2 \text{ and } a_2 = k_3/k_2\text{)}$$

THE CORRECT ANSWER IS (C)

CHEMICAL AM SOLUTIONS

134. From the Ideal Gas Law: $P_AV = N_ART$

$$C_A = N_A/V \quad \text{and} \quad P_A = C_ART$$

Therefore $-dP_A/dt = kP_A^2$ becomes $-RT\, dC_A/dt = k(C_ART)^2$

Or $\quad -dC_A/dt = kRTC_A^2$ and $\quad T = 100°F = 560°R$

So that the rate constant in $ft^3/(\text{lb mole-hr})$ is kRT

$$kRT = \frac{0.2}{\text{atm-hr}} \times \frac{0.7302\ ft^2\text{-atm}}{\text{lb mole-R}} \times 560°R$$

$$= 81.8\ ft^3/(\text{lb mole-hr})$$

THE CORRECT ANSWER IS (B)

135. Notation: $\quad [\ ] = $ activity and $(\ ) = $ mol/L

$$K_1 = \frac{[H^+][H_2PO_4^-]}{[H_3PO_4]} = \frac{(H^+)\gamma_\pm (H_2PO_4^-)\gamma_\pm}{(H_3PO_4)\gamma\, u} = 7.516 \times 10^{-3}$$

$$= \frac{(x)0.8(x)0.8}{(1-x)1.0} = 7.516 \times 10^{-3}$$

Rearranging into quadratic form:

$$0.64\, x^2 + (7.516 \times 10^{-3})x - (7.516 \times 10^{-3}) = 0$$

Solving with the quadratic formula:

$$x = \left[-7.516 \times 10^{-3} \pm \sqrt{(7.516 \times 10^{-3})^2 - 4(0.64)(-7.516 \times 10^{-3})} \right] / 2(0.64)$$

$$= \left[-7.516 \times 10^{-3} \pm 0.138915 \right] / 2(0.64) = 0.1027$$

So that $(H_2PO_4^-) = 0.1027$

THE CORRECT ANSWER IS (B)

136. If free Al is present, it will be oxidized to $Al_2O_3(s)$. This is verified by the value of $-\Delta G°/RT$ being very large.

That is, for $4/3\ Al + O_2 \leftrightarrow 2/3\ Al_2O_3$

It is $\dfrac{-700,000\,J/mol}{[8.314\ J/(mol\cdot K)](1,873°K)} = 44.95 = \ln\left[(a_{Al_2O_3})^{2/3}/(a_{Al})^{4/3}\right]$

So that $(a_{Al_2O_3})/(a_{Al})^2 = 1.92 \times 10^{29}$

The relative melting point temperatures also confirm this. All free aluminum would be in the molten liquid state at the reaction temperature and therefore free to be oxidized to Al_2O_3, which is a solid at the reaction temperature.

THE CORRECT ANSWER IS (C)

137. **Method One – Full Derivation:**
Reference: Levenspiel, *Chemical Reaction Engineering*, 2nd ed., Wiley, 1972, p. 109, Eqn. 17, Ch. 5.

$$\tau_{PFR} = C_{A_0}\int_0^{X_A}[dX_A/(-r_A)]$$

Substituting:

$$\tau_{PFR} = C_{A_0}\int_0^{X_A}\frac{dX_A}{-r_A} = C_{A_0}\int_0^{0.9}\frac{dX_A(1+k_2C_A)}{k_1C_A} = C_{A_0}\int_0^{0.9}\frac{dX_A}{k_1C_A} + C_{A_0}\int_0^{0.9}\frac{k_2}{k_1}dX_A$$

$$= \frac{C_{A_0}}{k_1}\int_0^{0.9}\frac{dX_A}{C_{A_0}(1-X_A)} + \frac{C_{A_0}k_2}{k_1}\int_0^{0.9}dX_A = \frac{1}{k_1}\left[-\ln(1-X_A)\right]\Big|_0^{0.9} + \frac{C_{A_0}k_2}{k_1}X_A\Big|_0^{0.9}$$

$$= \frac{1}{k_1}(-\ln 0.1) + \frac{C_{A_0}k_2}{k_1}(0.9)$$

$$= \left(\frac{1}{15\ hr^{-1}}\right)(2.303) + \frac{(0.25\ lb\ mole/ft^3)(16\ ft^3/lb\ mole)(0.9)}{15\ hr^{-1}} = 0.394\ hr$$

Method Two – Integrated equation:
Reference: Levenspiel, *Chemical Reaction Engineering*, 2nd ed., Wiley, 1972, p. 109, Eqn. 58a, Ch. 5.

$$\ln(C_{A_0}/C_A) + k_2(C_{A_0} - C_A) = k_1\tau$$

$$C_{A_0} = 10\ C_A = 0.25\ lb\ mole/ft^3$$

$$\ln(10) + 16\ ft^3/lb\ mole\ (0.25 - 0.025) = (15/hr)\ \tau$$

$$2.303 + 3.6 = 15\ \tau$$

$$\tau = 0.394\ hr$$

THE CORRECT ANSWER IS (B)

138. The first and third reactions are fast. Therefore, the concentration of the C·B complex is the concentration of C_0, or 7 kmol/m^3. At 30% conversion, the concentration of A is:

$$C_A = C_{A_0}(1 - X_A)$$
$$= 50(1 - 0.3) = 35 \text{ kmol/m}^3$$
$$-r_A = kC_A C_{(C·B)}$$
$$= [1.2 \times 10^{-6} \text{ m}^3/\text{kmol·s})](35 \text{ kmol/m}^3)(7 \text{ kmol/m}^3)$$
$$= 2.94 \times 10^{-4} \text{ kmol}(\text{m}^3·\text{s})$$

THE CORRECT ANSWER IS (C)

139. The method of solution follows suggestions in Levenspiel, *Chemical Reaction Engineering*, 2nd ed., Wiley, 1972. Equation, page, and chapter numbers referred to below are for this reference. Numerous other standard texts on reaction engineering treat these subjects in similar fashion.

For N mixed reactors (CSTRs) in series and a first-order reaction:

$$N \tau_i = (N/k) \times \left[(C_0/C_N)^{1/N} - 1 \right] \qquad \text{(Eqn. 6b, p. 137, Ch. 6)}$$

τ_i = space time in **each** reactor

C_0 = initial concentration of C

C_N = concentration of C at outlet of Nth reactor

For this case:

$C_N = 0.2\, C_0$ for 80% conversion

$N = 2$

$k = 0.0095 \text{ sec}^{-1}$

So that:

$$(2)\tau_i = (2/0.0095 \text{ sec}^{-1}) \times [(C_0/0.2\, C_0)^{1/2} - 1]$$
and $\tau_i = 130 \text{ sec} = 2.2 \text{ min}$

THE CORRECT ANSWER IS (A)

140. Temperature:

By Arrhenius' Law, a rate constant $k = k_0 \, e^{-E/RT}$, where E is the activation energy.

Therefore the rate of a reaction with a larger activation energy will increase more with temperature, so that raising the temperature would favor Reaction 1.

Concentration:

Since the rate of Reaction 1 is proportional to the square of the SO_2 concentration, and the rate of Reaction 2 is proportional to the first power of the SO_2 concentration, raising the SO_2 concentration would favor Reaction 1.

Therefore the correct strategy is to increase both the reaction temperature and the concentration of SO_2 in the feed.

THE CORRECT ANSWER IS (A)

Answers to the Chemical PM Practice Exam

Detailed solutions to each question begin on the next page.

501	D	**521**	B
502	D	**522**	D
503	B	**523**	B
504	B	**524**	D
505	C	**525**	B
506	A	**526**	C
507	C	**527**	C
508	C	**528**	C
509	B	**529**	B
510	B	**530**	B
511	A	**531**	A
512	C	**532**	D
513	A	**533**	A
514	A	**534**	C
515	A	**535**	B
516	D	**536**	C
517	A	**537**	B
518	C	**538**	A
519	C	**539**	A
520	D	**540**	D

501. In order to minimize cross-contamination between the different grades and brands, it is desirable to have plug-flow, i.e., velocity constant across the cross section:

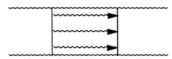

The more turbulent the flow, the closer the velocity profile is to plug flow. For that reason, highly turbulent flow will minimize the cross-contamination. For laminar flow, the velocity profile is parabolic, so that the fluid in the center of the pipe flows faster, thus moving ahead into the previous grade or brand. This will result in the most cross-contamination.

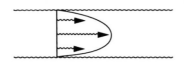

THE CORRECT ANSWER IS (D)

502. The frictional head loss is given by the following equation:

$$F = 2f \frac{L}{D} \frac{v^2}{g_c}$$

where F = frictional head loss
        f = Fanning friction factor
        L = equivalent length of the pipe
        D = diameter of the pipe
        v = linear velocity of flow (ft/sec)
       g_c = gravitational constant

For steady flow of an incompressible fluid with no pump work and no change in elevation, the Bernoulli equation reduces to: $F = -\dfrac{\Delta P}{\rho}$

where F = frictional head loss
    ΔP = pressure drop
    ρ = fluid density

Setting the two equations equal: $-\dfrac{\Delta P}{\rho} = 2f \dfrac{L}{D} \dfrac{v^2}{g_c}$

Rearranging, $-\Delta P = 2\rho f \dfrac{L}{D} \dfrac{v^2}{g_c}$

502. **(Continued)**

The linear flow velocity is obtained from the volumetric flow rate as follows:

$$v = \frac{4Q}{\pi D^2}$$

where v = linear velocity of flow (ft/sec)

Q = volumetric flow rate (ft^3/sec)

D = diameter of the pipe

Substituting and assuming that the Fanning friction factor does not change significantly with the change in pipe size (highly turbulent),

$$\Delta P = 2\rho f \frac{L}{D g_c}\left(\frac{16\,Q^2}{\pi^2 D^4}\right) = \frac{\text{Const}}{D^5}$$

Thus:

$$\frac{\Delta P_2}{\Delta P_1} = \left(\frac{D_1}{D_2}\right)^5 = \left(\frac{6.065}{3.068}\right)^5 = 30.19$$

$$\Delta P_2 = \Delta P_1 \times 30.19 = 1\,\text{psi} \times 30.19 = 30.19\,\text{psi}$$

THE CORRECT ANSWER IS (D)

503. For laminar flow of a liquid in a circular pipe, the Reynolds number must be less than 2,100. The equation for the Fanning friction factor f for laminar flow is $f = \dfrac{16}{\text{Re}}$,

where Re is the Reynolds number, $\text{Re} = \dfrac{DV\rho}{\mu}$

D = pipe diameter

V = linear velocity of flow

ρ = liquid density

μ = viscosity of the liquid

The friction factor is inversely proportional to the Reynolds number and thus decreases as the Reynolds number increases. The Reynolds number does not depend on the roughness of the pipe and neither does the friction factor.

The Reynolds number depends on the linear velocity of flow, so the friction factor also depends on the velocity.

THE CORRECT ANSWER IS (B)

504. First calculate r_H from the information given:

$$r_H = \frac{\text{void volume of the bed}}{\text{surface area of the packing}}$$

To calculate the total surface area of the packing, multiply the surface area of one particle by the number of particles. The number of particles can be calculated from the total volume occupied by the particles divided by the volume of a single particle:

$$S_{\text{pack}} = S_{\text{part}} \frac{V_b(1-\varepsilon)}{V_{\text{part}}}$$

where

V_b = volume of the empty bed

ε = bed porosity

S_{pack} = surface area of the packing

S_{part} = surface area of one particle

V_{part} = volume of one particle

$\frac{S_{\text{part}}}{V_{\text{part}}}$ is also called the specific surface of a particle, S_p.

Hydraulic radius, $r_H = \dfrac{V_b\varepsilon}{S_p V_b(1-\varepsilon)} = \dfrac{\varepsilon}{(1-\varepsilon)S_p}$

$$S_p = \frac{4\pi r^2}{\frac{4}{3}\pi r^3} = \frac{3}{r} = \frac{6}{D}$$

where r = particle radius

D = particle diameter

$$r_H = \frac{\varepsilon}{(1-\varepsilon)S_p} = \frac{\varepsilon D}{6(1-\varepsilon)} = \frac{(0.32)(4\text{ mm})}{6(1-0.32)} = 0.314\text{ mm} = 0.00103\text{ ft}$$

Interstitial velocity, $u_b = \dfrac{v}{\varepsilon} = \dfrac{4Q}{\pi D_b^2 \varepsilon} = \dfrac{4(30\text{ ft}^3/\text{min})}{\pi(2\text{ ft})^2(0.32)} = 29.84\text{ ft/min} = 0.50\text{ ft/sec}$

where Q = volumetric flow rate

v = superficial velocity (as if the bed were empty)

D_b = bed diameter

$$\text{Re} = \frac{4r_H u_b \rho}{\mu} = \frac{4(0.00103\text{ ft})(0.50\text{ ft/sec})(62.4\text{ lb/ft}^3)}{(1\text{ cP})\left[6.72 \times 10^{-4}\text{ lb/(ft-sec-cP)}\right]} = 191.3$$

THE CORRECT ANSWER IS (B)

505. At 30 psig, from steam tables:

$V_v = 9.46 \, \text{ft}^3/\text{lb}$ and $V_L = 0.0172 \, \text{ft}^3/\text{lb}$

where V_v = volume of the vapor

V_L = volume of the liquid

Knowing that the flow is 3% vapor and 97% liquid by weight, calculate the volumetric flow rate for each phase:

$Q_V = 0.03 \times 90,000 \, \text{lb/hr} \times 9.46 \, \text{ft}^3/\text{lb} = 25,542 \, \text{ft}^3/\text{hr} = 7.095 \, \text{ft}^3/\text{sec}$

$Q_L = 0.97 \times 90,000 \, \text{lb/hr} \times 0.0172 \, \text{ft}^3/\text{lb} = 1,501.56 \, \text{ft}^3/\text{hr} = 0.4171 \, \text{ft}^3/\text{sec}$

where Q_v = volumetric flow rate of the vapor

Q_L = volumetric flow rate of the liquid

The minimum cross-sectional area for flow of each phase, based on the maximum velocities for the vapor and for the liquid, can be calculated as follows:

$A_{V,\,min} = 7.095 \, \text{ft}^3/\text{sec} \times \dfrac{1}{100 \, \text{ft/sec}} = 0.07095 \, \text{ft}^2$

$A_{L,\,min} = 0.4171 \, \text{ft}^3/\text{sec} \times \dfrac{1}{15 \, \text{ft/sec}} = 0.02781 \, \text{ft}^2$

where $A_{V,\,min}$ = minimum required area for flow of the vapor

$A_{L,\,min}$ = minimum required area for flow of the liquid

Adding the two, the minimum area A_{min} is:

$A_{min} = 0.09876 \, \text{ft}^2$

The cross-sectional area for flow in a 4-in. Sch. 40 pipe is 0.0884 ft², which is too small.

The cross-sectional area for flow in a 6-in. Sch. 40 pipe is 0.2006 ft², which is larger than the minimum area.

THE CORRECT ANSWER IS (C)

506. For the constant, adiabatic, and isothermal flow of an incompressible fluid, a form of the Bernouilli equation is:

$$\frac{P_1}{\rho_1} + \frac{v_1^2}{2g_c} + \frac{h_1 g}{g_c} + h_{\text{pump}} = \frac{P_2}{\rho_2} + \frac{v_2^2}{2g_c} + \frac{h_2 g}{g_c} + h_f$$

where h_f = friction head

h_{pump} = pump head

ρ = density

P = pressure

v = linear velocity of flow (ft/sec)

g_c = gravitational constant

If the change in velocity is negligible, the equation reduces to:

$$h_{\text{pump}} = \frac{P_2}{\rho_2} - \frac{P_1}{\rho_1} + \frac{(h_2 - h_1)g}{g_c} + h_f$$

$$= \frac{(14.7 \ \text{lb/in}^2)(144 \ \text{in}^2/\text{ft}^2)}{(62.4 \ \text{lb/ft}^3)1.2} - \frac{(74.7 \ \text{lb/in}^2)(144 \ \text{in}^2/\text{ft}^2)}{(62.4 \ \text{lb/ft}^3)} + 225 \ \text{ft} + 25 \ \text{ft} = 105.88 \ \text{ft}$$

Converting,

$$h_{\text{pump}} = \frac{105.88 \ \text{ft} \ (50 \ \text{gal/min})(0.13368 \ \text{ft}^3/\text{gal})(62.4 \ \text{lb/ft}^3)}{33,000 \text{ft} \ \text{lb/(min-hp)}} = 1.34 \ \text{hp}$$

THE CORRECT ANSWER IS (A)

507. The frictional head loss is given by the following equation:

$$F = 2f \frac{L}{D} \frac{v^2}{g_c}$$

where F = frictional head loss
f = Fanning friction factor
L = equivalent length of the pipe
D = diameter of the pipe
v = linear velocity of flow (ft/sec)
g_c = gravitational constant

Both streams go to atmosphere, so they have the same pressure drop. They come from the same source, so they have the same density. Thus the head loss is the same for both streams:

$$F_1 = F_2$$

$$2f \frac{L_1}{D_1} \frac{v_1^2}{g_c} = 2f \frac{L_2}{D_2} \frac{v_2^2}{g_c}$$

Rearranging and canceling common terms,

$$\frac{v_2^2}{v_1^2} = \frac{L_1}{L_2} \frac{D_2}{D_1}$$

or:

$$v_2 = \sqrt{\frac{L_1 D_2}{L_2 D_1}} v_1$$

Substituting the values given:

$$v_2 = \sqrt{\frac{500 \text{ ft}(4.026 \text{ in.})}{400 \text{ ft}(3.068 \text{ in.})}} \, v_1 = \sqrt{1.6403} \, v_1 = 1.281 \, v_1$$

THE CORRECT ANSWER IS (C)

508. The brake horsepower for the pump (bhp) can be calculated from the total dynamic head (TDH) read from the pump curve, as follows:

$$\text{bhp} = \frac{Q(\text{TDH})\rho}{\eta_p}$$

where Q = volumetric flow rate
ρ = density of the fluid
η_p = efficiency of the pump

For 50 gal/min and a 9 1/2-in. impeller, from the pump curve, TDH = 82 ft and η_p is 0.29. Then:

$$\text{bhp} = \frac{(50 \text{ gal/min})(82 \text{ ft})1.1(62.4 \text{ lb/ft}^3)}{(7.481 \text{ gal/ft}^3)\left[33,000 \text{ ft-lb/(min-hp)}\right](0.29)} = 3.93 \text{ hp}$$

THE CORRECT ANSWER IS (C)

509. To find the pump head, set up the mechanical energy balance between the surface of the reservoir and the discharge of the pump:

$$\frac{P_1}{\rho} + \frac{v_1^2}{2g_c} + \frac{z_1 g}{g_c} + h_{\text{pump}} = \frac{P_2}{\rho} + \frac{v_2^2}{2g_c} + \frac{z_2 g}{g_c} + h_f$$

where h_f = friction head

h_{pump} = pump head

ρ = density

P = pressure

v = linear velocity of flow (ft/sec)

g = acceleration of gravity

g_c = gravitational constant

z = elevation

Calculate the linear velocity leaving the pump, using the cross-sectional area for flow (A) in a 6 in. Sch. 80 pipe:

$$v_2 = \frac{Q}{A} = \frac{4 \text{ ft}^3/\text{sec}}{0.181 \text{ ft}^2} = 22.1 \text{ ft/sec}$$

where Q = volumetric flow rate.

For no change in elevation, rearranging the first equation gives:

$$h_{\text{pump}} = \frac{P_2 - P_1}{\rho} + \frac{v_2^2 - v_1^2}{2g_c} + h_f$$

Substituting,

$$h_{\text{pump}} = \frac{(90 - 0)\text{lbf/in}^2 (144 \text{ in}^2/\text{ft}^2)}{62.4 \text{ lbm/ft}^3} + \frac{(22.1 \text{ ft/sec})^2 - 0^2}{2\left(32.2 \dfrac{\text{ft-lbm}}{\text{lbf-sec}^2}\right)} + 2 \text{ ft-lbf/lbm}$$

$$= 207.7 + 7.6 + 2 \text{ ft-lbf/lbm} = 217.3 \text{ ft-lbf/lbm}$$

THE CORRECT ANSWER IS (B)

CHEMICAL PM SOLUTIONS

510. The measured pressure drop can be broken into three parts:

$$\Delta P_{nozzles} = 1 \text{ psi (inlet)} + 1 \text{ psi (outlet)} = 2 \text{ psi}$$

$$\Delta P_{static} = \rho \frac{g}{g_c} \Delta z = (62.4 \text{ lb/ft}^3)(32.2 \text{ ft/sec}^2)[(\text{lbm-sec}^2)/(32.2 \text{ ft-lbf})](4.67 \text{ ft})(\text{ft}^2/144 \text{ in}^2) = 2.02 \text{ psi}$$

$$\Delta P_{exchanger} = \text{function of head loss and internal configuration}$$

Pressure drops for the nozzles and static head are unchanged by exchanger passes, so they will be the same before and after.

$$\Delta P_{measured} = \Delta P_{nozzles} + \Delta P_{static} + \Delta P_{exchanger}$$

$$\Delta P_{exchanger\ 1} = 6 \text{ psi} - 2 \text{ psi} - 2.02 \text{ psi} = 1.98 \text{ psi}$$

$$= 2\rho f \frac{L_1}{D} \frac{v_1^2}{g_c} \text{ from head loss relation}$$

Assume the friction factor is nearly the same before and after for fully turbulent flow typical of heat exchangers. If the exchanger is changed from two passes to four passes, the water flows through half as many tubes but twice the length, thus doubling the velocity:

$$L_2 = 2L_1 \text{ and } v_2 = 2v_1$$

$$\Delta P_{exchanger\ 2} = 2\rho f \frac{L_2}{D} \frac{v_2^2}{g_c} = 2\rho f \frac{2L_1}{D} \frac{(2v_1)^2}{g_c} = 8\left(2\rho f \frac{L_1}{D} \frac{v_1^2}{g_c}\right) = 8 \Delta P_{exchanger\ 1}$$

$$\Delta P_{measured\ 2} = \Delta P_{nozzles} + \Delta P_{static} + \Delta P_{exchanger\ 2}$$

$$= 2 \text{ psi} + 2.02 \text{ psi} + 8(1.98 \text{ psi})$$

$$= 19.86 \text{ psi}$$

THE CORRECT ANSWER IS (B)

511. From *Perry's Chemical Engineers' Handbook*, the permanent pressure loss in an orifice with standard pipe tap locations (vena contracta taps) is given by:

$$1 - R = \frac{p_1 - p_3}{p_1 - p_2}$$

where R = recovery fraction

$1 - R$ = permanent loss fraction

p_1 = pressure upstream of the orifice

p_2 = pressure at the vena contracta, just downstream of the orifice, where the pressure is lowest

p_3 = pressure far downstream of the orifice

511. **(Continued)**

For turbulent flow, $1 - R$ can be estimated as $1 - \beta^2$, where β is defined as the ratio of the orifice diameter to the pipe diameter, $\beta = D_o/D$.

$$\beta = D_o/D = 1.6 \text{ in.}/4 \text{ in.} = 0.4$$

$$1 - R = 1 - \beta^2 = 1 - (0.4)^2 = 0.84$$

$p_1 - p_2$ is calculated from the manometer reading as follows:

$$p_1 - p_2 = \frac{(\rho_m - \rho)\Delta h}{\rho} = \frac{\left(848.6 \text{ lb/ft}^3 - 62.4 \text{ lb/ft}^3\right)24 \text{ in.}}{62.4 \text{ lb/ft}^3}(0.0361 \text{ psi/in. H}_2\text{O}) = 10.92 \text{ psi}$$

where ρ_m = density of the manometer fluid
ρ = fluid density
Δh = height of the manometer column

Then, from the first equation, the permanent pressure loss, $p_1 - p_3$, is:

$$p_1 - p_3 = (1 - R)(p_1 - p_2) = 0.84(10.92 \text{ psi}) = 9.17 \text{ psi}$$

THE CORRECT ANSWER IS (A)

512. Option (C) is correct since the design of a venturi is such that it minimizes turbulence. This reduces the friction losses, resulting in a lower permanent pressure drop.

Option (A) is false because, for the same flow rate, the pressure drop for a venturi would be lower since it creates less turbulence than an orifice.

Option (B) is false because a venturi is more expensive than an orifice, because of its more specialized construction.

Option (D) is false because the coefficient of discharge for a venturi is higher than that for an orifice, because of the lower turbulence.

THE CORRECT ANSWER IS (C)

513. Rearranging the equation given in the problem statement:

$$\mu = \frac{\Gamma}{2\pi r^2 L(dv/dr)}$$

The velocity of the fluid v varies from the radial velocity of the bob at the bob's surface to zero at the inside edge of the cup. At the surface of the bob, the radial velocity is:

$$v = 2\pi r\omega = 2\pi(2\text{ cm})(10\text{ min}^{-1}) = 125.66\text{ cm/min}$$

where ω = rotational velocity of the bob, 10 rpm.

Because the fluid is Newtonian, the velocity profile is linear and dv/dr can be calculated as the difference in velocity divided by the difference in radius:

$$\frac{dv}{dr} = \frac{0 - 125.66\text{ cm/min}}{2.05\text{ cm} - 2\text{ cm}} = -\frac{125.66\text{ cm/min}}{0.05\text{ cm}} = -2,513\text{ min}^{-1}$$

Substituting in the first equation,

$$\mu = \frac{\Gamma}{2\pi r^2 L(dv/dr)} = \frac{(7,500\text{ dyne·cm})(60\text{ sec/min})}{2\pi(2\text{ cm})^2(10\text{ cm})(2,513\text{ min}^{-1})} = 0.712\text{ dyne·sec/cm}^2$$

THE CORRECT ANSWER IS (A)

514. $H_{CO_2}(25°C) = 35.4\text{ atm/(mol/kg)}$

$p_{CO_2} = 0.000354\text{ atm}$

Henry's law applied to dilute solutions of A, i.e., $x_A \rightarrow 0$:

$$p_A = x_A H_A(T)$$

x_A = mole fraction of A in liquid phase, moles/mole

c_A = concentration of A, moles/kg

For Henry's law constant based on concentration rather than activity in the liquid phase,

$$p_A = c_A H_A(T)$$

Therefore,

$$c_{CO_2} = \frac{p_{CO_2}}{H_{CO_2}(T)}$$

$$c_{CO_2} = \frac{0.000354\text{ atm}}{35.4\text{ atm/(mol/kg)}} = 0.00001\text{ mol/kg}$$

THE CORRECT ANSWER IS (A)

515. Vapor pressure of 2-propanol is given by:

$$\ln P^{\text{sat}} = 8.8 - \frac{1,311.86}{t + 33.06}$$

where P^{sat} = vapor pressure, psia

t = temperature, °F

At 176°F, 2-propanol and water form an azeotropic mixture.

Activity coefficient of 2-propanol in the azeotropic mixture is $\gamma = 1.08$.

At equilibrium for an azeotrope, liquid and vapor compositions are equal, $x_i = y_i$.

For non-ideal solutions, $y_i P_{\text{total}} = \gamma_i x_i P_i^{\text{sat}}$

With $x_i = y_i$, $P_{\text{total}} = \gamma_i P_i^{\text{sat}}$

$$\ln P^{\text{sat}} = 8.8 - \frac{1,311.86}{t + 33.06} = 8.8 - \frac{1,311.86}{176 + 33.06} = 8.8 - 6.275 = 2.525$$

$$P^{\text{sat}} = 12.49 \text{ psia}$$

$$P = 1.08 \times 12.49 \text{ psia} \times \frac{1 \text{ atm}}{14.7 \text{ psia}} = 0.918 \text{ atm}$$

THE CORRECT ANSWER IS (A)

CHEMICAL PM SOLUTIONS

516. This question is solved graphically using the ternary diagram provided:

1. Draw the operating line. The operating line goes through the feed point and the bottoms point. The distillate composition is not given in the question statement but has to be located on the operating line.

2. To determine the distillate composition:
   The organic distillate product is given on the graph. It is located on the solubility curve, but not on the operating line. This indicates that the distillate product will separate into two phases: organic and aqueous. The point on the diagram that represents the aqueous phase must be:
   - On the solubility curve
   - On the other side of the plait point
   - On the other side of the operating line than the organic distillate

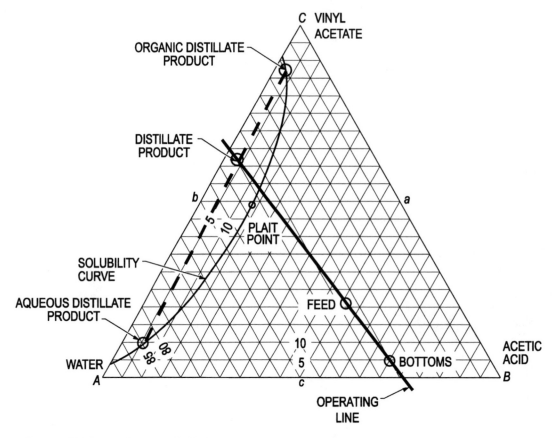

From the available options, only (D) satisfies these requirements.

THE CORRECT ANSWER IS (D)

517. Since ethane is more volatile (i.e., has a lower boiling point) than heptane, increasing the ethane concentration will lower the dew point of the mixture. The dew point is the temperature at which a vapor first begins to condense.

THE CORRECT ANSWER IS (A)

518. Given:

Vapor from the bottom tray, y_1	0.70
Vapor from the reboiler, y_B	0.75
Liquid from the bottom tray, x_1	0.90
Bottom product, x_B	0.95

Evaluate the L/V ratio in the stripping section of a column given compositional data at the bottom tray and the kettle reboiler. The stripping section operating line starts at $y_B = x_B = 0.95$. Thus, the following is obtained:

$$L = V + B$$

$$B = L - V$$

$$L \times x_1 = V \times y_B + B \times x_B = V \times y_B + (L - V)x_B = V \times y_B + L \times x_B - V \times x_B$$

$$L(x_1 - x_B) = V(y_B - x_B)$$

$$\frac{L}{V} = \frac{y_B - x_B}{x_1 - x_B} = \frac{0.75 - 0.95}{0.90 - 0.95} = \frac{-0.20}{-0.05} = 4.00$$

THE CORRECT ANSWER IS (C)

519. Given:

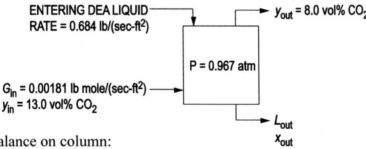

CO$_2$ balance on column:

$$G_{in} \times y_{in} - G_{out} \times y_{out} = L_{out} \times x_{out}$$

$$G_{in} \times y_{in} = 0.00181 \text{ lb mole/(sec-ft}^2) \times 0.13 = 0.0002353 \text{ lb mole/(sec-ft}^2)$$

Balance on the carrier gas:

$$G_{out} = G_{in} \frac{1 - 0.13}{1 - 0.08} = 0.00181 \text{ lb mole/(sec-ft}^2) \times \left(\frac{0.87}{0.92}\right) = 0.0017116 \text{ lb mole/(sec-ft}^2)$$

$$G_{out} \times y_{out} = 0.0017116 \text{ lb mole/(sec-ft}^2) \times (0.08) = 0.00013693 \text{ lb mole/(sec-ft}^2)$$

$$L_{in} = 0.684 \text{ lb/(sec-ft}^2) \times (\text{lb mole/24 lb}) = 0.0285 \text{ lb mole/(sec-ft}^2)$$

$$CO_2 \text{ absorbed} = 0.0002353 \text{ lb mole/(sec-ft}^2) - 0.00013693 \text{ lb mole/(sec-ft}^2)$$

$$= 0.00009837 \text{ lb mole/(sec-ft}^2)$$

$$x_{out} = \frac{CO_2 \text{ absorbed}}{L_{out}} = \frac{CO_2 \text{ absorbed}}{CO_2 \text{ absorbed} + L_{in}}$$

$$= \frac{0.00009837 \text{ lb mole/(sec-ft}^2)}{0.00009837 \text{ lb mole/(sec-ft}^2) + 0.0285 \text{ lb mole/(sec-ft}^2)} = 0.00344$$

THE CORRECT ANSWER IS (C)

520. Reference: Green and Perry, *Perry's Chemical Engineers' Handbook*, 8th ed., McGraw-Hill, ©2008.

p. 14-29, Table 14-5: A sieve tray has a "2:1 turndown ratio. Not generally suitable for operation under variable loads." The number of passes does not affect the turndown ratio significantly.

p. 14-29, Table 14-5: A fixed valve tray has a "2.5:1 turndown ratio. Not generally suitable for operation under variable loads."

p. 14-34, Other Tray Types, Bubble-Cap Trays: Bubble-cap trays have "a unique ability to operate at very low gas and liquid rates."

p. 14-47: "Turndown...*Sieve and fixed valve trays* have a poor turndown ratio (about 2:1). Turndown of *moving valve trays* is normally between about 4:1 to 5:1. Special valve designs can achieve even better turndown ratios...."

THE CORRECT ANSWER IS (D)

521. Overhead product, $x_D = 0.8$ (given)
The equation for the rectifying section operating line is:

$$y_{n+1} = \frac{L}{V} x_n + \left(1 - \frac{L}{V}\right) x_D$$

The slope L/V is internal reflux ratio.

In terms of external ratio L_o/D:

$$\frac{L}{V} = \frac{L_o}{L_o + D} = \frac{L_o/D}{L_o/D + 1}$$

Let $R = L_o/D$, so $R_{min} = \left(L_o/D\right)_{min}$.

Substituting,

$$y_{n+1} = \frac{R}{R+1} x_n + \left(1 - \frac{R}{R+1}\right) x_D = \frac{R}{R+1} x_n + \left(\frac{R+1-R}{R+1}\right) x_D = \frac{R}{R+1} x_n + \left(\frac{1}{R+1}\right) x_D$$

$$y = \frac{R_{min}}{R_{min}+1} x + \frac{x_D}{R_{min}+1}$$

From the graph, pivoting the rectifying operating line at $x_D = 0.8$, tangent to the equilibrium line to get the pinch point, the y-intercept is 0.325.

Therefore at $x = 0$,

$$y = \frac{x_D}{R_{min}+1}$$

$$\therefore R_{min} = \frac{x_D}{y} - 1 = \frac{0.8}{0.325} - 1 = 1.46$$

521. **(Continued)**

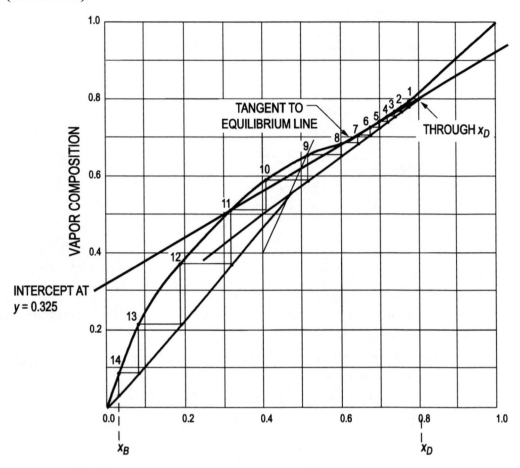

THE CORRECT ANSWER IS (B)

CHEMICAL PM SOLUTIONS

522. Reference: Bennett and Myers, *Momentum, Heat, and Mass Transfer*, 3rd ed., Chapter 31: Convective Mass Transfer Coefficients—Application to a Packed Tower—Dilute Solutions.

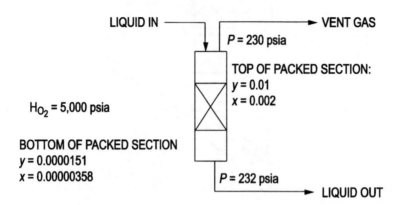

The following notation applies:

z = height of tower, ft

L = mole velocity of liquid phase/flux, lb mole/(hr-ft^2)

k_x^o = individual mass-transfer coefficient, liquid phase, lb mole/(hr-ft^2) The superscript means the coefficient applies to a dilute solution.

a = interfacial area per unit volume of contacting device, ft^2/ft^3

H_{OL} = height of overall transfer unit, liquid phase, ft

n_{OL} = number of overall transfer units, liquid phase (dimensionless)

K_x = overall mass transfer coefficient, lb mole/(hr-ft^2)

$$z = \frac{L}{k_x^o a} \times \frac{x_{AO} - x_{A1}}{\left(x_A^* - x_A\right)_{lm}}$$

$$z = H_{OL} n_{OL}$$

$$H_{OL} = \frac{L}{K_x a}$$

For dilute solutions, $K_x = k_x^o$

$$H_{OL} n_{OL} = \frac{L}{K_x a} n_{OL} = \frac{L}{k_x^o a} \times \frac{x_{AO} - x_{A1}}{\left(x_A^* - x_A\right)_{lm}}$$

$$n_{OL} = \frac{x_{AO} - x_{A1}}{\left(x_A^* - x_A\right)_{lm}}$$

Solving for this question:

$$n_{OL} = \frac{x_{O_2, \text{top}} - x_{O_2, \text{bottom}}}{\Delta x_{O_2, lm}}$$

$$\Delta x_{O_2, lm} = \frac{\left(x_{O_2, \text{top}} - x^*_{O_2, \text{top}}\right) - \left(x_{O_2, \text{bottom}} - x^*_{O_2, \text{bottom}}\right)}{\ln \dfrac{x_{O_2, \text{top}} - x^*_{O_2, \text{top}}}{x_{O_2, \text{bottom}} - x^*_{O_2, \text{bottom}}}}$$

522. (Continued)

$$p_{O_2} = H_{O_2} \times x^*_{O_2}$$

$$y_{O_2} = \frac{p_{O_2}}{P}$$

$$x^*_{O_2} = \frac{y_{O_2} \times P}{H_{O_2}}$$

$$x^*_{O_2, \text{top}} = \frac{y_{O_2, \text{top}} \times P_{\text{top}}}{H_{O_2}} = \frac{(0.01)(230 \text{ psia})}{5,000 \text{ psia}} = 0.00046$$

$$x^*_{O_2, \text{bottom}} = \frac{y_{O_2, \text{bottom}} \times P_{\text{bottom}}}{H_{O_2}} = \frac{(0.000151)(232 \text{ psia})}{5,000 \text{ psia}} = 0.00000070$$

$$\left(x_{O_2, \text{top}} - x^*_{O_2, \text{top}}\right) = 0.002 - 0.00046 = 0.00154$$

$$\left(x_{O_2, \text{bottom}} - x^*_{O_2, \text{bottom}}\right) = 0.00000358 - 0.00000070 = 0.00000288$$

$$\Delta x_{O_2, lm} = \frac{(0.00154) - (0.00000288)}{\ln \dfrac{0.00154}{0.00000288}} = 0.0002447$$

$$n_{OL} = \frac{0.002 - 0.00000358}{0.0002447} = 8.16$$

THE CORRECT ANSWER IS (D)

523. Given:

Packing factor, F_p = 32 ft^{-1}
Water flow rate, L' = 10.35 lb/sec
Gas flow rate, G' = 8.34 lb/sec
Liquid viscosity, μ = 1.11 cP
ΔP / (Height of column) = 1.0 in. H$_2$O/ft of packing
Densities:

$$\text{Gas, } \rho_G = 0.0909 \text{ lb/ft}^3$$
$$\text{Liquid, } \rho_L = 62.4 \text{ lb/ft}^3$$

$$x_{\text{axis}} = \left(\frac{L}{G}\right)\sqrt{\frac{\rho_G}{\rho_L}} = \frac{\dfrac{L'}{A}}{\dfrac{G'}{A}}\sqrt{\frac{\rho_G}{\rho_L}} = \frac{\dfrac{10.35}{A}}{\dfrac{8.34}{A}}\sqrt{\frac{0.0909}{62.4}} = 0.0474$$

From the figure

$$y_{\text{axis}} = 0.085 = \frac{G^2 F_p \psi \mu^{0.2}}{\rho_G \rho_L g}$$

$$G^2 = \frac{0.085 \rho_G \rho_L g}{F_p \psi \mu^{0.2}}$$

The ratio of liquid densities ψ equals 1 since the absorbing fluid is water.

$$G^2 = \frac{(0.085)(0.0909)(62.4)(32.2)}{(32)(1)(1.11)^{0.2}} = 0.475$$

$$G = 0.6893 \text{ lb/(ft}^2\text{-sec)}$$

$$\text{Area} = \frac{G'}{G} = \frac{8.43}{0.6983} = 12.10 \text{ ft}^2 = \frac{\pi D^2}{4}$$

$$D = \sqrt{\frac{(12.10)(4)}{\pi}} = 3.93 \text{ ft}$$

THE CORRECT ANSWER IS (B)

CHEMICAL PM SOLUTIONS

524. Given:

10,000 lb/hr AIR
(H_2S FREE BASIS)
0.001 lb H_2S/lb AIR → 7,100 lb GAC → 2×10^{-6} lb H_2S/lb AIR

MINIMUM H_2S CONCENTRATION IN THE GAC IS
0.0005 lb H_2S/lb GAC AFTER REGENERATION

Determine saturation of H2S on the GAC at the maximum influent concentration.

$$Y^* = 855 \times X^* + 0.05 = 855(0.001) + 0.05 = 0.905 \text{ lb } H_2S/\text{lb GAC}$$

H2S holding capacity by the GAC during a run,

$$7,100 \text{ lb GAC } (0.905 - 0.0005) \text{ lb } H_2S/\text{lb GAC} = 6,422 \text{ lb } H_2S$$

Rate of H2S entering GAC bed,

$$10,000 \text{ lb air/hr } (0.001 - 2 \times 10^{-6}) \text{ lb } H_2S/\text{lb air} = 9.98 \text{ lb/hr } H_2S$$

Time to fully saturate the bed,

$$t = \frac{6,422 \text{ lb } H_2S}{9.98 \text{ lb } H_2S/\text{hr}} = 643 \text{ hr}$$

THE CORRECT ANSWER IS (D)

525. The present value (PV) of a future sum of money (F) depends on the interest rate (i) [the value of money], and the number of intervals (n) over which the interest on the future payment would be compounded. This is expressed as follows: $P = F/(1 + i)^n$. As the time frame of this problem is only 5 years, it may be solved by calculating the present value of each future payment ($400,000 per year) and the future salvage recovery at the end of year 5 ($100,000), summing them, and subtracting the initial cash investment required ($900,000).

$$PV = (\$400,000) \sum_{n=1}^{n=5} 1/(1 + 0.07)^n + (\$100,000)/(1 + 0.07)^5 - \$900,000$$

$$= (\$400,000)(4.1002) + \$71,299 - \$900,000 = \$811,379$$

Alternatively, the present value of a stream of equal future payments at a constant interest rate may be more efficiently calculated, particularly for longer periods, using a formula available in many financial accounting books and *Perry's Chemical Engineers Handbook*, 7th ed., p. 9-13, yielding the same result as the summation term for the annual payments above.

$$P = A\left[(1+i)^n - 1\right]/i(1+i)^n \text{ where } n \text{ is the number of years of payments } (A).$$

$$P = (\$400,000)[(1.07)^5 - 1]/0.07(1.07)^5 = \$400,000(0.402552)/0.07(1.402552) = \$1,640,080$$

Adding salvage and subtracting initial cost as above:

$$\$1,640,080 + \$71,299 - \$900,000 = \$811,379$$

THE CORRECT ANSWER IS (B)

CHEMICAL PM SOLUTIONS

526. The ANSI/ISA standard S5.1-1984 (R1992) *Instrumentation Symbols and Identification* defines how each symbol is constructed using graphical elements, alpha and numeric identification codes, abbreviations, function blocks, and connecting lines. Two publications that provide an overview of the standard are the August 2000 issue of *Control Engineering* and the May 2009 issue of *Chemical Engineering Progress*. In this standard, P in the first position denotes pressure, which eliminates Options A and B. As the determination of pH requires an analysis, the letter *A* in the first position is proper. The letter *E* in the second position denotes "sensor" (primary element), but the problem statement calls for local display. Therefore, the second letter should be *I*, which stands for "indication" when used in the second position.

THE CORRECT ANSWER IS (C)

527. The reboiler is at equilibrium stage, which is 100% efficient.
The actual number of trays = (4.3 – 1) / 0.45 = 7.33 trays ~ 8 trays
Eight trays equal seven tray spaces, each with a tray spacing of 36 in.:

$$(36 \text{ in.}) \times (1 \text{ ft}/12 \text{ in.}) \times (7) = 21 \text{ ft}$$

Space above top tray   = 1 tray spacing = 3 ft
Space below bottom tray   = 2 tray spacings = 6 ft
Straight side height   = 21 + 3 + 6 = 30 ft

THE CORRECT ANSWER IS (C)

528. The reboiler boilup ratio (V/B) is determined by an overall material balance and an ammonia material balance. The feed (F) quantity is equal to the sum of the quantity of the bottoms (B) and the quantity of the distillate (D), i.e., F = B + D. The vapor flow (V) is equal to the distillate flow (D), i.e., V = D, since it is a stripping column (no reflux). Ammonia in the feed is equal to the sum of the ammonia in D and B, or

$$0.4F = 0.95V + 0.01B$$
$$0.4(B + V) = 0.95V + 0.01B$$
$$0.39B = 0.55V$$
$$V/B = 0.39/0.55 = 0.71$$

THE CORRECT ANSWER IS (C)

529. The question statement suggests that the rupture disk discharge will be a multiphase mixture of reactive materials, potentially hazardous to personnel. Because the discharge is multiphase, it should be directed to a blowdown tank for separation of the liquids and solids prior to venting the gas. As there is no assurance that the gas is harmless, the blowdown tank vent should be directed to the flare. The solids and liquids, if discharged directly to the flare header, might plug or otherwise damage the flare system. Discharge 10 ft above the reactor would rain down solids and/or liquids on people and equipment in the vicinity. Discharge at grade level would subject anything in the vicinity to the gases as well as the solids and/or liquids. From the question statement, it is a reasonable expectation that the disk discharge would be hot enough to be thermally hazardous, requiring confinement in a blowdown tank before venting the gases.

THE CORRECT ANSWER IS (B)

530. According to OSHA 3138-01R 2004, a confined space:

    1. Is large enough for an employee to enter fully and perform assigned work
    2. Is not designed for continuous occupancy by the employee; and
    3. Has a limited or restricted means of entry or exit.

These spaces may include underground vaults, tanks, storage bins, pits and diked areas, vessels, silos, and other similar areas.

The equipment described in I, II, and IV, but not III falls within the definition of a confined space. The electrical room (III) does not satisfy conditions 2 or 3 in the OSHA standard. Occupancy of I, II, or IV during normal operation could result in serious injury or death, whereas occupancy of III during normal operation is anticipated.

THE CORRECT ANSWER IS (B)

531. Use Boyle's Law to calculate the change in volume:

$$p_1 V_1 = p_2 V_2$$

Calculate pressure at the surface and at the outlet of the bubbler tube:

Liquid height above the bubbler tube, h = 12 ft × 80% − 1 ft = 8.6 ft

Absolute pressure :

$$p_{out} = p_{atm} + 8.6\ \text{ft} \times 62.4\ \text{lb/ft}^3 \times 0.85 \times 1\ \text{ft}^2 / 144\ \text{in}^2$$
$$= 14.7\ \text{psia} + 3.17\ \text{psia}$$
$$= 17.87\ \text{psia}$$

$$p_{surf} = p_{atm} = 14.7\ \text{psia}$$

Percent expansion :

$$\left(\frac{V_{surf}}{V_{out}} - 1 \right) \times 100\% = \left(\frac{p_{out}}{p_{surf}} - 1 \right) \times 100\% = \left(\frac{17.87\ \text{psia}}{14.7\ \text{psia}} - 1 \right) \times 100\% = 21.56\%$$

THE CORRECT ANSWER IS (A)

532. In general, it is best to use a method that manipulates a variable physically as close as possible to the controlled variable. It is apparent from the diagram that the gas space in the condenser is primarily filled with DMS and water, which are, to a large extent, removed by the cryo trap and non-condensables. Observe that the air bleed injection is between the cryo trap and the vacuum pump. Controlling the pressure by manipulating the air bleed control valve (V-4) (a non-condensable) will minimize variations in flow through the cryo trap and will provide the fastest pressure response with a simple control logic. The pressure in the column, using the signal from PT-2, is best controlled by adjusting the setting of the air bleed control valve V-4. The effect on process conditions other than the pressure will be minimal. A common disadvantage of all of the other options is the potential for increasing the amount of water going to the cryo trap and plugging it.

Further, relying on changes in heat transfer is slow, and manipulating the amount of steam or refrigerant may upset the column equilibrium. The energy balance will require a change in heat load in one to be matched by a change in the other. The whole column is affected by a change in either heat load. The pressure response is further slowed by the inertia of the column.

Changing the pump speed will affect the flow through the cryo trap and the pressure drop across it. The inertia of the drive and pump will slow the rate of response. The pressure drop across the cryo trap will oppose the pressure adjustment in the column. The control logic is made more complex by using the vacuum pump speed controller to control column pressure and may overload the cryo trap with water. Variable-speed vacuum pumps are rarely employed for vacuum distillation operations.

Reference: Sloley, Andrew W., Effectively Control Column Pressure, *Chemical Engineering Progress*, January 2001, pp. 40-48.

THE CORRECT ANSWER IS (D)

533. Guidance published in *Perry's Chemical Engineers' Handbook*, 6th ed., p. 23-31, Table 23-2, and p. 23-34 through p. 23-38, Table 23-3, indicate copper and mild steel are unsuitable for this service, but Type 316 stainless steel would be suitable for the conditions specified. These tables are in earlier editions of *Perry's* but have been greatly condensed in editions after the 6th.

Tables in the later editions of *Perry's* continue to provide sufficient guidance to arrive at an answer for this question, but provide less precise description of the conditions of the process fluid concentration and temperature than prior editions. The 7th edition provides Table 28-2 on p. 28-30 and p. 28-31, and show mild steel and copper as unsuitable for nitric acid. Stainless steel of the composition typical of type 316 has an excellent to good rating. Guidance in somewhat greater depth is available in "*Metallic materials: physical, mechanical, and corrosion properties*" by Philip A. Schweitzer.

THE CORRECT ANSWER IS (A)

534. Non-destructive techniques are comprehensively described in ASTM standards, and a brief overview of radiographic, ultrasonic, and dye penetrant inspections appear on p. 10-149 in *Perry's Chemical Engineers' Handbook*, 7th ed. Sounding is described in ASTM D 4580-03, *Standard Practice for Measuring Delamination in Concrete Bridge Decks*.

Sounding would not be applicable to a pump impeller. Ultrasonic techniques and radiography require sophisticated equipment and highly skilled technicians for their use and interpretation. Ultrasonic inspection would be further complicated by the convoluted surfaces and varying thicknesses of a pump impeller. Dye penetrant techniques are suitable for field application, easily implemented, and simple enough for application by the average worker. Although dye penetrant inspection is limited to the detection of flaws on visually accessible surfaces, that is the stated objective in this instance.

THE CORRECT ANSWER IS (C)

535. The pump discharge is composed of a mixture of 2 gpm of HF acid and 1 gpm of seal liquid for a total of 3 gpm, with an apparent specific gravity of:

$$(2 \text{ gpm} \times 1.2 + 1 \text{ gpm} \times 0.7)/3 \text{ gpm} = 1.03$$

To adjust for specific gravity: ft/psi of discharge fluid is $2.31/1.03 = 2.24$ ft/psi

The difference between vessel pressure and pump suction is 5 psi or 11.2 ft.
The head developed in ft of discharge fluid must be 11.2 ft + 10 ft elev. + 1 ft loss = 22.2 ft.

Referring to the centrifugal pump performance diagram and interpolating between the curves, it can be seen that a 5 1/4-in.-diameter impeller will develop a head only slightly over 20 ft at 3 gpm, while a 5 1/2-in.-diameter impeller will develop a head between 22 ft and 23 ft at 3 gpm. The 5 1/4-in.-impeller would be inadequate, so the choice is the 5 1/2-in.-impeller.

THE CORRECT ANSWER IS (B)

536. Cumulative production = production rate × hours of operation:

1. Average production rate per cycle $= Q = \int_0^\tau 100(1 - e^{-(10 - 0.1x)})dx/(\tau + 4)$

    where τ = production hours after a filter bag change, and 4 = hours of downtime for the change. Thus:

2. $Q = [100\,\tau - 100\,e^{-10}(10)\,e^{0.1\,\tau}]/(\tau + 4)$

The fastest approach is to proceed with a trial and error calculation because the choices are limited to the four answers provided.

For 50, $\tau =$ 46, and $Q = [4,600 - 1,000\,e^{-5.4}]/50 = 91.91$

For 72, $\tau =$ 68, and $Q = [6,800 - 1,000\,e^{-3.2}]/72 = 93.88$

For 76, $\tau =$ 72, and $Q = [7,200 - 1,000\,e^{-2.8}]/76 = 93.94$

For 104, $\tau = 100$, and $Q = [10,000 - 1,000\,e^0]/104 = 86.54$

The calculations would reduce to three if started at 104.

The classical approach would be to convert the variable to:
T (cycle time) $= \tau + 4$ and set the differential to zero; then solve by trial and error.

$$Q = [100(T - 4) - 100\,e^{-10}(10)e^{0.1(T - 4)}]/T = 100 - 400/T - 1,000\,e^{-10.4} \times e^{0.1T}/T$$

$$Q = 100 - 400/T - 0.0304\,e^{0.1T}/T$$

Using the identity, $d(uv) = vdu + udv$ and letting $u = e^{0.1T}$; $v = 1/T$, then:

$$d(e^{0.1T}/T) = -e^{0.1T}/T^2 + 0.1\,e^{0.1T}/T, \text{ and}$$

$$dQ/dT = 400/T^2 - 0.0304[-e^{0.1T}/T^2 + 0.1T\,e^{0.1T}/T^2]$$

The differential of transformed equation (2) set to zero reduces to $e^{0.1T}(0.1T - 1) = 13,144$
The solution is $T = 75.97$.

THE CORRECT ANSWER IS (C)

CHEMICAL PM SOLUTIONS

537. The specified design requirement for the containment dike is the failure of any one tank, as all tanks are the same size. The floor area of the tank that fails is available for inclusion in the area available for the secondary containment of the spilled volume. The determination of the height of the dike that surrounds a tank farm 100 ft × 100 ft that contains four tanks, each 30 ft in diameter and 30 ft high, for the condition of a single tank failure follows.

Containment area: 100 ft × 100 ft = 10,000 ft^2
Adjusted floor area for 3 intact tanks: $10,000 - 3 \times \pi(30^2/4) = 10,000 - 2,121 = 7,879$ ft^2
Single tank volume: $\pi(30^2/4) \times 30 = 21,206$ ft^3

Height of dike:
Volume = 21,206 ft^3 = 7,879 × h
$h = 21,206/7,879 = 2.691$ ft

THE CORRECT ANSWER IS (B)

538. A calculation confirms that all of the toluene available evaporates into the room.

The saturation pressure is given as 20 mm Hg at the ambient temperature P = 20/760 atm.
gm = MW(20/760)(10 × 10 × 3)/R (273.15 + 18.4) = 30,362 or 30.36 kg, which is far greater than the amount of available toluene; therefore all 2 kg of toluene will become vapor.

The term ppm is an acronym for parts per million. In the context of airborne gaseous pollutant concentrations, it stands for volumes of gaseous pollutant per million volumes of air. Note that the question specifies "ppmv."

Let V_t = volume of toluene vapor, and then ppmv = $(V_t/\text{Total Volume}) \times 10^6$
The room is at 1 atmosphere, so
$$\text{ppmv} = (2,000/92)(8.205 \times 10^{-5})(273.15 + 18.4) \times 10^6 / 300 \text{ m}^3 = 1,734$$

An alternate formula is:
$$\text{ppmv} = (\text{mg/m}^3)(273.15 + {}^\circ\text{C})/(12.187)(\text{MW}), \text{ which gives the same answer.}$$

THE CORRECT ANSWER IS (A)

539. The reaction has consistently been completed in about 8 hours. If it were actually a first-order reaction, as assumed, it would have been substantially more than 75% complete after 6 hours when the vent valve was closed. The relief valve sized for the initial rate of the first-order reaction would have been more than adequate to limit the pressure in the vessel near the end of the reaction cycle. If the first-order reaction rate was higher than that used to size the relief valve, the reaction would have been even nearer completion at the time the vent valve was closed. If the problem was too low a solvent level and there was no autocatalytic reaction, at the higher initial concentration a first-order reaction would have proceeded more rapidly and been nearer completion at the time the vent valve was closed. The stirrer could generate some additional heat, but heat losses from the uninsulated reactor in conjunction with the relief valve would have limited the pressure rise. The temperature difference between the vessel and its surroundings would have increased about 50% at a vessel pressure of 30 psig. The most likely cause of the explosion was that the reaction was not first order, but a more complex mechanism with a rapid increase in reaction rate near the end of the cycle.

THE CORRECT ANSWER IS (A)

540. The Resource Conservation and Recovery Act (RCRA) is a U.S. law that provides, in broad terms, the general guidelines for the waste management program envisioned by Congress. It includes a congressional mandate directing EPA to develop a comprehensive set of regulations to implement the law. The hazardous waste program, under RCRA Subtitle C, establishes a system for controlling hazardous waste from the time it is generated to its ultimate disposal—in effect, from "cradle to grave."

EPA regulations, or rulemakings, translate the general mandate of RCRA into a set of requirements for the agency and the regulated community. The RCRA hazardous waste program regulates commercial businesses as well as federal, state, and local government facilities that generate, transport, treat, store, or dispose of hazardous waste. 40 CFR Part 260 contains all of the RCRA regulations governing hazardous waste identification, classification, generation, management, and disposal.

The Clean Air Act regulates air emissions, OSHA regulates workplace safety, and NPDES regulates water emissions.

THE CORRECT ANSWER IS (D)

PE Practice Exams Published by NCEES

Civil: Construction

Civil: Geotechnical

Civil: Structural

Civil: Transportation

Civil: Water Resources and Environmental

Electrical and Computer: Computer Engineering

Electrical and Computer: Electrical and Electronics

Electrical and Computer: Power

Environmental

Mechanical: HVAC and Refrigeration

Mechanical: Mechanical Systems and Materials

Mechanical: Thermal and Fluids Systems

Structural Engineering

For more information about these and other NCEES publications and services, visit NCEES.org or call Client Services at (800) 250-3196.